THE ROLE OF A SYLLABUS IN FLYING TRAINING

Most states have an aviation authority responsible for, among other matters, deciding which subjects must be understood by those training for a pilots' licence. Over the past quarter of a century the range of these subjects has grown considerably so that learning to fly, even when the student has no intention of becoming a professional pilot, is no longer as simple a matter as it was prior to the 1939–1945 war.

To ensure that all subjects and items within those subjects are taught during the course the value of a syllabus of training has in recent years assumed growing importance. It may be regarded as a shopping list of knowledge to be acquired but it has more to offer than that. A syllabus of flying training ensures:

(a) that the concept of the course is understood by the student and the instructor.

(b) that the content is known by all concerned with the course of training.

(c) that progress during the course may be monitored.

(d) that space is provided where the student may record the instructor's comments after each lesson. These are of value during revision and subsequent practice.

(e) that a summary of learning and practice is available to both student and instructor, thus ensuring that the course has been completed.

Flight Briefing for Pilots, Vols. 1, 2 and 3, have been written to conform with a Syllabus of Flying Training for the Private Pilots' Licence and the IMC Rating (currently confined to the UK) that has been recognised by the UK Civil Aviation Authority. The syllabus is published by Longman.

Throughout the text headings published in this type **[Instrument Indications]** cross refer to the syllabus.

Books on Aviation by N. H. Birch and A. E. Bramson

Flight Briefing for Pilots series
Flying the VOR
A Guide to Aircraft Ownership
The Tiger Moth Story
Captains and Kings
Radio Navigation for Pilots
Flight Briefing for Microlight Pilots
Flight Emergency Procedures for Pilots

By Alan Bramson

Be a Better Pilot
Make Better Landings
The Book of Flight Tests
Master Airman, a biography of
    Air Vice-Marshal Donald Bennett CB, CBE, DSO, FRAeS
Principles of Flight (Audio-visual trainer)

By Neville Birch

The Instrument Rating
Passenger Protection Technology in Aircraft Accident Fires

Flight Briefing for Pilots

Volume 3
The IMC Rating and an introduction to the Instrument Rating

N. H. Birch MSc, PhD, MRAeS
Liveryman of the Guild of Air Pilots and Air Navigators

and A. E. Bramson FRAeS
Past Chairman of the Panel of Examiners
Liveryman of the Guild of Air Pilots and Air Navigators

Illustrated by A. E. Bramson

SECOND EDITION

Longman Group UK Limited,
Longman House, Burnt Mill, Harlow,
Essex CM20 2JE, England
and Associated Companies throughout the world.

Published in the United States of America
by Longman Inc., New York

First published in Great Britain 1981
Reprinted 1985
Second edition 1988

British Library Cataloguing in Publication Data

Birch, N. H.
    Flight briefing for pilots. —— 2nd ed.
    Vol. 3: The IMC rating and an introduction
    to the instrument rating
    1. Airplanes —— Piloting
    I. Title   II. Bramson, A.E.
    629.132′52   TL710

ISBN 0-582-98883-7

Set in AM Comp/Set 10/12 Times Roman

Produced by Longman Singapore Publishers (Pte) Ltd.
Printed in Singapore

Contents

Contents

Preface

When Volume 1 of this series first appeared in 1961 most private pilots were trained to map reading their way across country. It was the only method because radio was a rare luxury and usually confined to a communications set with a limited number of frequencies.

Since those days the development of transistors and micro-miniaturization has made possible an entirely new breed of lightweight radio, some of it offering facilities similar to the type of equipment found on public transport aircraft. Used correctly such equipment enables a pilot to navigate accurately when weather conditions prevent map reading and to land safely in reduced visibility or conditions of low cloud.

It would be reasonable to expect that the availability of modern radio equipment would have reduced the number of weather-induced accidents but, in many countries, the reverse is the case. This, of course, is surprising but unfortunately human nature has not improved at the same rate as technology. Fill a light aircraft with black boxes, support it with a good flight panel and there are those among us who will delude themselves that '... come bad weather I can cope with the help of all this equipment'. What these worthies fail to realize is that even the best equipment is worthless in unskilled hands.

For many years the basic PPL course of training included no instrument flying and many inexperienced pilots regarded it as of little consequence. In an effort to discourage 'do-it-yourself' participation in this demanding form of flying a brief demonstration, aimed at convincing the student pilot of the futility of relying on the senses, was introduced towards the end of the course. It was also intended to encourage more inexperienced pilots to take instrument flying instruction.

In an ideal world all pilots would have an Instrument Rating but in the UK this is a difficult and expensive qualification to acquire. Then there was the need to consider the rights of many private pilots who aspire to no more than flying around the local area on a bright, sunny day – surely a perfectly reasonable pastime. To them a mandatory Instrument Rating would be unnecessary, difficult and expensive to acquire and probably impossible to maintain. On the other hand, many private pilots use light aircraft for serious touring and, if an Instrument Rating might be too expensive and time-consuming for them to contemplate, clearly some form of instrument flying skill, recognized by the issue of a rating, would be an advantage.

So far, the UK is the only country to introduce a special instrument qualification to pilots seeking to improve their skills without having to attain the professional standards demanded of an Instrument Rating. It was in 1970 that the first *IMC Rating* was introduced by the UK Civil Aviation Authority. In essence, pilots with only a basic PPL were subjected to a number of new weather restrictions. To restore the privileges which previously allowed unskilled, low-hours pilots to fly when common prudence said '*stay on the ground*', the IMC Rating course had to be completed and the flying test passed.

By the late 1970s the scope of the IMC Rating had been enlarged and to cater for the needs of pilots taking the course *Flight Briefing for Pilots, Volume 7* was written by the authors and published in 1981. It was a self-contained manual, repeating text that already existed in *Vols 1 to 4* of the series. Early in 1986 the first two volumes of the totally revised and, in the main, re-written *Flight Briefing for Pilots* series were published. *Volumes 1 and 2* cover the course for the basic PPL and it is assumed that the student using this book during training for the IMC Rating will have read them in the course of gaining a PPL. To avoid repeating text on such matters as weight and balance, airfield performance, basic meteorology etc., this book is confined to explaining instrument flying and the various radio aids.

This manual, like *Volumes 1 and 2* in the series, is written to conform with the UK CAA-recognized syllabus of training for the PPL and the IMC Rating published by Longman. Many of the items of knowledge listed in the IMC Rating syllabus will already have been covered in the PPL course but, for the purpose of revision, page references are given so that the relevant text can easily be found in *Vols 1 and 2*.

At the end of the course, when the ground and air tests have been passed, the IMC Rating will make you a safer pilot, capable of flying when the weather grounds holders of no more than a basic PPL. It is also a valuable step towards a full Instrument Rating.

NHB
AEB

List of Abbreviations

ADF	Automatic Direction Finding Equipment
ADR	Advisory Route
AFIS	Aerodrome Flight Information Service
AIC	Aeronautical Information Circular
AIS	Aeronautical Information Service
ATA	Actual Time of Arrival
ATCC	Air Traffic Control Centre
ATD	Actual Time of Departure
ATS	Air Traffic Service
ATIS	Automatic Terminal Information Service
ATZ	Aerodrome Traffic Zone
BFO	Beat Frequency Oscillator
CTA	Control Area
CTR	Control Zone
D/F	Direction Finding
DH	Decision Height
DME	Distance Measuring Equipment
EAT	Expected Approach Time
ETA	Estimated Time of Arrival
ETD	Estimated Time of Departure
FIC	Flight Information Centre
FIR	Flight Information Region

FIS	Flight Information Service
FL	Flight Level
FM	Fan Marker
GP	Glide Path
HF	High Frequency
Hmr	Homer
IAP	Instrument Approach Procedure
IFR	Instrument Flight Rules
ILS	Instrument Landing System
IMC	Instrument Meteorological Conditions
ISA	International Standard Atmosphere
IM	Inner Marker
LARS	Lower Airspace Radar Service
LF	Low Frequency
LOC	Localizer (ILS)
LOM	Locator/Outer Marker
M	Magnetic
MATZ	Military Aerodrome Traffic Zone
Met	Meteorology
mb	millibar (equivalent to hPa [hectopascals])
MDH	Minimum Descent Height
MF	Medium Frequency
MHz	megahertz
Mkr	Marker
MM	Middle Marker
MSA	Minimum Safe Altitude
msl	mean sea-level
NDB	Non Directional Beacon
OAT	Outside Air Temperature

OCH	Obstacle Clearance Height
OCL	Obstacle Clearance Limit
OM	Outer Marker (ILS)
OBS	Omni-bearing selector (VOR)
PAPI	Precision Approach Path Indicator
PAR	Precision Approach Radar
QDM	Magnetic heading to station (zero wind)
QFE	Altimeter setting to show vertical height above airfield
QGH	Letdown procedure using VHF/DF
QNH	Altimeter setting which would cause the altimeter to read airfield elevation on the ground
QTE	True bearing
R	Radial
RMI	Radio Magnetic Indicator
RTF	Radio Telephony
RVR	Runway Visual Range
SID	Standard Instrument Departure
SIGMET	Significant meteorological phenomena
SRA	Surveillance Radar Approach
SRE	Surveillance Radar Element
SRZ	Special Rules Zone
SSR	Secondary Surveillance Radar
STAR	Standard Instrument Arrival Route
SVFR	Special VFR Flight
TAF	Terminal Aerodrome Forecast
TMA	Terminal Control Area
UHF	Ultra High Frequency
UIR	Upper Flight Information Region

VASI	Visual Approach Slope Indicator
VDF	VHF Direction Finding
VFR	Visual Flight Rules
VHF	Very High Frequency
VMC	Visual Meteorological Conditions
VOLMET	Airfield Information broadcast continuously
VOR	VHF Omni-directional Radio Range

Air Exercises — Basic Stage

Chapter 1
Exercise 19
Instrument Flying (Revision)

The basis of instrument flying was outlined in *Instrument Flying* (*Appreciation*) on pages 299 to 319 of Volume 1 in this series. The purpose of this chapter is to revise the student's knowledge and suggest various methods of improving basic instrument flying skill.

The ability to fly accurately on instruments is the very foundation of radio navigation; without this foundation a pilot is in no position to contemplate the use of radio aids since they are of little value unless he is able to fly the aircraft safely without the advantages of outside visual references. Like any skill, instrument flying can best be improved with practice. However, practice misapplied is likely to result in a waste of flying hours and money to little avail. The following text is intended to provide practical advice on how to obtain the best results from this practice.

It is essential that good standards of instrument flying are achieved before attempting to fly the radio procedures.

Methods of Practising Basic Instrument Flying

Several programs for use with personal or home computers are available. In the main, the symbols generated on the screen are of poor quality and methods of simulating aircraft control range from a series of buttons at worst to a control stick (with no rudder pedals or throttle) which may, or may not, react like a real aircraft. Although one or two better computer programs are becoming available they must be chosen with care.

Simulators

Simulators used for training airline crews are capable of reproducing most of the sensations of flight via six-degree movement. They can provide good pictorial representation of a selection of airports, simulate all emergencies and have a flight deck that cannot be distinguished from the real aircraft. Those intended for training pilots of light/general aviation aircraft are very much simpler. They can take the form of a small desk top panel with a control wheel and throttle or a more comprehensive simulator with all controls, the type of radio installation one would expect to find in a well equipped executive aircraft and an instructor's glass-top desk which includes a mechanical 'crab' capable of tracing the track being flown in relation to a large map.

Usually, general aviation category simulators are more difficult to 'fly' accurately than the real aircraft. Provided the simulator does not handle so badly that it bears no relationship to reality this can be an advantage in so far as the trainee is made to work hard if accurate standards are to be achieved.

The most obvious advantage of simulator training is the reduction in cost but the ability to stop an exercise, virtually in 'mid air', and discuss why it is going wrong is something that cannot be done in a real aircraft. The simulator is ideal for learning the various procedures and improving instrument flying skill.

Of the 15 hours' dual instrument flying instruction required during the IMC Rating Course two hours may be completed in a simulator. But students experiencing difficulty in coping with basic instruments and the radio commands should invest in additional simulator time before spending more money in an aircraft.

Instrument Flying Practice in an Aircraft

If instrument flying training is to be of value the student must obviously be prevented from seeing out of the aircraft while relying on the eyes of a safety pilot/instructor to ensure separation from other aircraft, etc. Various methods of curtailing the trainee's vision without prejudice to that of the safety pilot have been used in the past but the most common methods now in use are:

(a) **Hoods:** Purpose designed caps with large peaks which obscure external vision but allow the trainee to scan the instruments while the safety pilot maintains a good lookout.

(b) **Screens:** These take the form of slats which allow the safety pilot to look out of the aircraft but confine the trainee's vision to the instruments. Pilots under training for an Instrument Rating (as opposed to the IMC Rating) must use screens that have been approved by the aviation authorities.

Improving Basic Instrument Flying Skills

The most usual causes of poor instrument flying are:

(*a*) Incorrect method of reading the instrument panel
(*b*) Over-controlling
(*c*) Incomplete understanding of the information provided by the instruments singly and collectively
(*d*) Bad application of Power/Attitude flight techniques to achieve a required performance
(*e*) Inability to relax.

Reading the Instrument Panel

One school of thought believes that the flight panel should be read in its entirety, much as the word INSTRUMENT is recognized as a whole rather than letter-by-letter. However, the most widely accepted method entails reading the instruments relevant to the mode of flight at the time and the technique is explained under the heading *Selective Radial Scan*.

Correct Use of Controls

Because the instruments are small the attitude indications provided are likewise small. It is a basic rule of all instrument flying that changes from one mode of flight to another (e.g. from straight and level to climb, from one heading to another, etc.) must be made *gradually*.

All alterations in pitch and roll must be made with minimum control movements. In light aircraft it is essential that the control wheel/stick should be held in the fingers, not the fist. Only then will it be possible to take full advantage of accurate trim which, in a stable aircraft, can relieve the pilot of workload and allow more attention to be devoted to cockpit management – selection of radio frequencies/settings, reading the charts, etc.

The importance of accurate trim cannot be over-stressed.

Information Provided by the Instruments

For safe and accurate flight a pilot requires to know the attitude, performance and position of the aircraft (vertically and relative to a known position) throughout the flight. The source of this information is as follows:

Information provided	Primary indication	Secondary indication
PITCH	Attitude Indicator	ASI
		VSI
		Altimeter
ROLL	Attitude Indicator	Turn & Bal.
		DI
YAW	Balance Indicator	DI
PERFORMANCE		
Airspeed	ASI	—
Altitude	Altimeter	—
Rate of climb/descent	VSI	—
Rate of turn	Turn needle	—
AIRCRAFT POSITION	The various radio aids	

Read individually and collectively the gyro/pressure/radio-operated instruments mentioned in the table will give the pilot a constant and accurate statement of the aircraft's status at all times.

Power/Attitude Flight

At this stage it is opportune to remind the student of the old adage:

POWER + ATTITUDE = PERFORMANCE

What does this mean? To quote some examples, a light aircraft with the throttle set to deliver 100 HP when the aircraft is flying with its wings at 4° angle of attack may cruise at 100 kt in level flight (Fig. 1). Alter either power or angle of attack and there will be a different performance.

If power is increased while the airspeed is held at 100 kt angle of attack will remain at 4° but the flight path would be inclined upwards.

Fig. 1   Typical instrument panel display while flying at 4° Angle of Attack with cruising power.

Fig. 2   A power increase at the same Angle of Attack (IAS) as in Fig. 1 will result in a rate of climb and a nose-up attitude as shown on the Attitude Indicator.

The change in performance in this case would be the introduction of a climb (Fig. 2).

Alternatively, if power is left unchanged but attitude is changed to, say, 2° angle of attack the new performance would reflect an increase in airspeed and a loss of height. If required, the new airspeed could be held while power was added until height was being maintained to achieve level flight at a higher airspeed. In practice pilots carry out these adjustments as instinctively as a motorist changing gear but the concept of **Power + Attitude = Performance** is of prime importance while flying on instruments to specific speeds and rates of climb/descent.

It therefore follows that instrument flying can be made easier if the pilot learns the approximate power settings for various phases of flight, e.g. maximum rate of climb, economic cruise, descent without flap, approach in the landing configuration, etc. Naturally these settings vary from one aircraft type to another. But the pilot who knows, for example, that with full flap at 70 kt a throttle setting of 2000 RPM will produce a 500 ft/min rate of descent will cope more easily with an instrument approach than one who must experiment with the power.

The Ability to Relax

If full advantage is to be taken of accurate trim, so that the aircraft is flown with only minor corrections, the control wheel/stick must be handled lightly. During instrument flight the pilot is required to fly accurate headings at a constant level and a prescribed airspeed. Charts must be consulted, radio equipment set up, radio commands followed and instructions from the Air Traffic Control Service acknowledged and complied with.

A tense pilot will most likely over-control and fly the aircraft erratically. Preoccupation with the basic need of maintaining altitude, airspeed and heading can only result in the neglect of other important functions.

Pre-flight Checks

The procedures to adopt before flight in VMC are explained in *Exercise 2. Preparation for and Action after Flight* (Vol. 1, p. 11). The IMC Rating allows pilots to take off and land when visibility is restricted to 1 n.m. and there is a low ceiling (600 ft minimum is recommended for an IMC Rated pilot who is in practice). Because of the icing risk the following additional items must be checked prior to the flight:

1. De-icing systems (when fitted) must be serviceable.
2. All radio equipment and instruments must be in working order.
3. All radio nav and approach charts, including those for the planned alternates if the destination is below weather limits, must be current.
4. Aerials, windscreens and all parts of the airframe must be free from ice.

The Risks of Airframe Ice

It is often not appreciated that even a thin layer of hoar frost on the wings of an aircraft can degrade the take-off performance of an aircraft or even prevent lift-off. There have been a number of serious accidents caused by pilots attempting the take-off with frost or a light covering of snow on the flying surfaces. Heavier icing that may have formed overnight can limit control movement by blocking the shrouds.

During the pre-flight checks it is essential that frost/ice is removed from the wings, tail surfaces and aerials before starting the engine(s). It is also important to ensure that all windows and the windscreen are clean.

Instrument Flying Revision

The following notes are intended to revise previous instrument flying training.

Selective Radial Scan

In this technique the Attitude Indicator is regarded as the 'Master Instrument'. Others forming the Basic 'T' flight panel are used to confirm and supplement its readings. Using the AI as the main reference the eyes should at intervals scan other instruments (according to mode of flight at the time) before returning to the AI (Fig. 3). Here is an example:

CLIMBING   Check **AI** for correct attitude.
Check **Turn Needle/Co-ordinator** for yaw.
Check **Ball** for balance.
Check **AI** for correct attitude.
Check **DI** for correct heading.
Check **AI** for correct attitude.
Check **Engine instruments** (overheating, RPM, etc).
Check **VSI** for rate of climb.
Check **Altimeter** for new altitude.
Check **AI** for correct attitude.

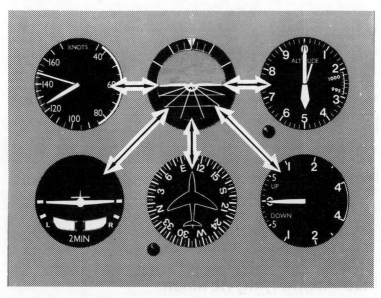

Fig. 3   The basis of Selective Radial Scan.

The scan described above is repeated as a continuous cycle until the transition from climb to straight and level flight is made. A modified scan may be required during other manoeuvres. With practice the Selective Radial Scan technique can become second nature.

Use of Attitude Indicator

Early versions of this instrument, which were usually known as Artificial Horizons, had toppling limits of 110° in roll and 60° in pitch. Later instruments have wider limits and, in some cases, complete freedom of movement in pitch and roll. Construction and operating principle of the instrument are described on pages 303–9 of *Flight Briefing for Pilots* (Vol. 2).

Modern AIs have a small knob for adjusting the alignment of the aircraft symbol in relation to the horizon line. This is to compensate for parallax errors (i.e. the apparent displacement of an object due to the angle of observation) that affect pilots of different eye levels relative to the instrument. Ideally the datum should be set during straight and level flight and, once set, it should not be altered.

Because of the limited size of the instrument changes in pitch attitude are represented by small movements of the horizon line and a nose-up or nose-down indication of little more than the thickness of the aircraft symbol's wings can relate to an airspeed change of 10 kt or more. Consequently, pilots must develop an eye for accurate reading of these minor but important pitch changes. A scale giving pitch angles at intervals of 5 and 10 degrees is usually provided.

Changes in the rolling plane are directly related to aircraft angle of bank and this may accurately be assessed by reading the scale provided around the top half of the instrument. The angle of bank scale is of particular value while setting up turns at various airspeeds (described under *The Standard Turn* and *Turning at Various Angles of Bank*).

The attitude indicator has an excellent reliability record and when instrument flying is essential because of the weather pilots must be prepared to place complete trust in this very accurate device.

Straight and Level Attitude Indications

The setting up of straight and level on instruments is much the same as for visual flight. When a particular speed is required (as opposed to setting everyday cruising RPM and trimming the aircraft so that it maintains altitude) this will be adjusted with reference to attitude (AI), applying sufficient power to maintain height/altitude.

SCAN: Check correct pitch attitude (AI). Check correct power (RPM indicator). Check height/altitude/flight level (VSI and altimeter).

Maintaining Heading

Inexperienced pilots often fail to understand that the slightest departure from lateral level in a modern aircraft will result in a turn towards the lower wing.

SCAN: Check lateral level (AI). Check heading (DI and Turn Indicator).

Maintaining Balanced Flight

Aircraft without an adjustable rudder trim will usually have a small fixed tab on the trailing edge of the rudder which is set on the ground. Fixed trim tabs can only be correctly adjusted for one flight condition and that will usually be cruising speed at 65–75 per cent power.

During the climb considerable rudder pressure will often be required to maintain balanced flight and that will be discussed under *Climbing and Descending*. However, a common fault among pilots who experience difficulty in relaxing while on instruments is to fly with 'crossed controls', e.g. the left wing has gone down a few degrees, a turn is indicated to the left and heading starts to decrease. To stop the turn right rudder is applied – a misuse of controls – and a skid to the left is bound to follow. The disadvantages are:

(*a*) Out-of-balance flight at low airspeeds and high power settings can develop into a spin (see *High Power/Low Speed* p. 131, Vol. 1). While this is more related to climbing than straight and level flight lack of balance is a bad habit to be avoided.

(*b*) Prolonged out-of-balance flying is uncomfortable for the passengers.

(*c*) Out-of-balance flight increases drag, reduces speed and will result in fewer air miles/gallon of fuel.

SCAN: Check lateral level (AI). Check balance (Ball) and if necessary centre it by applying rudder in the direction of displacement, e.g. ball to the left of centre – LEFT rudder. Check heading (DI).

Effect of Changes in Power and Configuration

An exercise of particular value is to practise changing airspeeds while maintaining a steady altitude. A considerable degree of skill is required and in the early stages most trainees experience difficulty in maintaining a steady altitude and heading while changing speeds.

It should be remembered that power alterations will, due to slipstream and torque effects, upset the balance of the aircraft. Assuming clockwise propeller rotation when seen from the cabin the addition of power will cause a swing to the left and a power reduction will induce a swing to the right.

The effects of power changes are compounded by alterations in pitch attitude. Add power and the nose will rise if unchecked. Reduce power and the nose will drop.

Changing Airspeed on Instruments

Provided the pilot remembers the yaw and pitch reactions to power changes the only other factor of importance is to recognize that, like any other vehicle, an aircraft requires time to accelerate and decelerate. Do not expect an immediate change of airspeed when the power is adjusted.

Reducing Airspeed

1. Bring back the throttle to the approximate power setting.
2. Prevent yaw with rudder.
3. Prevent loss of altitude with gentle back pressure on the wheel/stick. **Avoid over-controlling with excessive back pressure because this will cause the aircraft to climb.**
4. When the new airspeed is indicated hold that attitude on the AI, re-trim and check that the aircraft is neither climbing nor descending (VSI/Altimeter).
5. A climb indicates too much power. Reduce power slightly and if necessary re-trim.
6. A descent indicates insufficient power. Add a little more power and if necessary re-trim.

The practice just described should be extended to flight with various flap settings, taking care not to exceed the flap limiting speed. Pilots should aim to memorize the picture presented by the AI for the most commonly used modes of flight.

SCAN: Check wings level and correct cruising attitude (AI). Note that at low cruising speeds, flaps up, the aircraft symbol is above the horizon line and so forth. Check balance (Ball). Check heading (DI). Check altitude (Altimeter). Short-term departures from cruising level will be indicated on the VSI. When speeds or configurations are altered the engine instruments will be included in the scan.

Increasing Airspeed

1. Increase power to a setting related to the new airspeed.
2. Prevent yaw with rudder.
3. Prevent a climb with gentle forward pressure on the wheel/stick. *Avoid over-controlling since this could cause loss of height/altitude.*
4. When the new airspeed is indicated hold that attitude on the AI,

re-trim and check that the aircraft is neither climbing nor descending (VSI/Altimeter).

5. A climb indicates too much power. Throttle back slightly and if necessary re-trim.
6. A descent indicates insufficient power. Open the throttle slightly and re-trim.

SCAN: See *Reducing Airspeed.*

Climbing and Descending

As previously mentioned the transition from straight and level flight to the climb or descent must be made gradually. The effects on trim and balance of power changes should be anticipated during the following sequences of events:

From Straight and Level Flight to the Climb

1. Open the throttle to the correct climbing power. Check any tendency to yaw and keep the wings level.
2. Raise the nose slightly. Hold the new attitude and if necessary re-trim. In some aircraft the addition of power may automatically hold up the nose to the new attitude without need of trim adjustment.
3. Allow time for the airspeed to settle, then make fine adjustments to attitude as required until the correct speed is attained.

SCAN: Check wings level and nose-up attitude (AI). Check balance (Ball) and if necessary correct with rudder in the direction of displacement. Check that the required heading is being maintained (Turn Indicator and DI). Check the airspeed and during a prolonged climb monitor the engine instruments at intervals for signs of overheating.

From the Climb to Straight and Level Flight

1. At the correct height *slowly* lower the nose and allow the airspeed to increase *while maintaining the new altitude.* Do not reduce power at this stage but compensate for yaw with appropriate use of rudder.
2. Keep the wings level and as the ASI moves towards the correct speed move back the throttle to cruising power.
3. Re-trim, check heading, speed and power setting, remembering that changes in airspeed will affect engine RPM when the aircraft has a fixed-pitch propeller.

SCAN: Check wings level and on the horizon (AI), altitude correct and steady (Altimeter and VSI), balance (Ball) and heading (Turn Needle and DI). Check airspeed and engine RPM.

From Straight and Level Flight to Descent

1. Reduce power to the RPM known to give the required rate of descent, at the same time checking any yaw with rudder. Keep the wings level (AI).
2. When a descent is to be made at a lower than cruising speed (e.g. for an instrument approach) do not allow the nose to drop as power is reduced but apply a little back pressure to maintain the aircraft symbol on the horizon (AI). Speed will gradually reduce.
3. At the required descent speed allow the aircraft symbol to descend below the horizon and re-trim.
4. Check the rate of descent on the VSI. If it is too high add a little power and raise the nose slightly. When the descent rate is insufficient reduce power slightly and lower the nose. Re-trim as necessary.

SCAN: Check the wings are level and the nose is below the horizon (AI). Check for correct airspeed (ASI). Check rate of descent (VSI). Check balance (Ball). Check heading (Turn Indicator and DI). During prolonged descents at low power settings apply full carburettor heat at intervals.

Constant Rate Descents to given Altitudes

1. Commence a descent as previously described and attain the required rate of descent by adjusting the power. Allow time for the VSI to settle. If the rate is too high open the throttle slightly. When the rate is not fast enough reduce power a little. While making these adjustments check that the airspeed is remaining constant.
2. Anticipate the new height/altitude by 100–150 ft, then progressively add power.
3. As the speed increases *gradually* raise the nose and stop the descent. Check that the wings are level and prevent yaw with appropriate use of rudder.
4. Allow the airspeed to settle to the required figure, check that height is being maintained and if necessary adjust power/attitude to achieve this.
5. Re-trim and fine-adjust power if necessary.

SCAN: Check wings are level (AI). Check height/altitude (Altimeter and VSI). Check heading (DI). Check balance (Ball). Check airspeed (ASI). Check the engine instruments at intervals.

The Standard Turn

Turns forming part of instrument procedures are flown at Rate 1 or less and the Rate 1 turn has become known as the **Standard Rate Turn.** The Rate 1 turn entails changing heading at 3°/second, i.e. a reversal of direction through 180° will take one minute and two minutes are required to fly through 360°, hence the other term sometimes used for a Rate 1 turn: **2 Minute Turn**.

Turn Co-ordinators are usually confined to indicating Rate 1 or less whereas Turn and Balance Indicators of the two finger or needle and ball type will show Rates 1, 2, 3 and sometimes 4. However, from the instrument flying point of view it is more convenient for the pilot to adopt the correct angle of bank when setting up a Rate 1 turn. Bank angle for any rate is a function of airspeed and the following method of determining bank angle will prove sufficiently accurate for practical purposes:

Bank Angle for Rate 1 Turn = 10% IAS + 7

EXAMPLES: IAS 100 kt: Bank angle = 10 + 7 = 17°

IAS 130 kt: Bank angle = 13 + 7 = 20°

IAS 283 kt: Bank angle = 28 + 7 = 35°

The last example will explain why a passenger jet indicating 283 kt at 30,000 ft (TAS 450 kt on a standard day) must apply relatively steep bank angles to achieve a Rate 1 turn.

Entry to the turn is, like all instrument manoeuvres, made gradually and the sequence of events is as follows:

1. Determine the correct angle of bank as previously explained and apply aileron in the required direction. Apply sufficient rudder in the same direction to maintain balance (Ball). Some aircraft do not require rudder while turning. Be prepared for the aircraft to overbank and, when the correct angle is indicated on the AI, move the wheel/stick towards the ailerons neutral position.

2. Prevent loss of height with gentle back pressure on the wheel/stick while checking the VSI and altimeter. Note there is a slight decrease in airspeed (Fig. 4).

3. To resume straight and level flight apply aileron to level the wings

Fig. 4   Rate 1 Turn to the left. Note the slight reduction in IAS
from the 125 kt shown in Fig. 1.

with reference to the AI and remove any balancing rudder that
may have been applied.
4. Release back pressure on the wheel/stick as bank is decreasing
and the wings roll level.
5. Check height/altitude, heading and attitude.

SCAN: Check correct angle of bank and nose position (AI). Check
correct rate of turn (Turn needle). Check balance (Ball). Check
height/altitude (Altimeter/VSI). Check airspeed (ASI). Check for a
steady change in heading (DI).

Turning at Various Angles of Bank

There are occasions when turns of less than Standard Rate are an
advantage during instrument procedures. For example, there may be
a need to compensate for drift by turning at Rate ½ while closing with
a new heading. Obviously a Rate ½ turn will require less bank than a
Rate 1 and the Turn needle can be used to confirm that heading is
being changed at 1½°/second. A more accurate method of checking

17

turn rates entails the use of the stopwatch and this will shortly be described.

Turns at rates greater than Rate 1 are not used during the various instrument procedures.

Turns onto Selected Headings

There is a tendency among some pilots to continue turning until the new heading appears on the DI. At that point the roll-out is commenced. As a result, the aircraft will go through the required heading and it will be necessary to turn back by 10°–15°.

If the transition from turning to wings level is made correctly 5–8 seconds will elapse during the process according to bank angle. It therefore follows that when flying a light aircraft the roll-out should start some 15° before the new heading has been reached. With practice it is possible to arrive at the wings-level attitude as the new heading appears on the DI.

Timed Turns

Although bank angle confirmed by the turn needle will allow the pilot to fly a Rate ½ or Rate 1 turn with a reasonable degree of accuracy, for precision the stopwatch must be introduced.

Some pilots find it convenient to mark the stopwatch glass at 10 second intervals and add equivalent degrees for a Rate 1 turn as shown in the following table. Pens suitable for marking glass are available:

Watch Dial markings	Degree markings
10 sec.	30°
20 sec.	60°
30 sec.	90°
40 sec.	120°
50 sec.	150°
60 sec.	180°

The introduction of another instrument may at first appear to complicate the scanning process but practice will develop the ability to divide attention between the essential instruments while disregarding the inessential.

Climbing and Descending Turns onto Given Headings

Climbing and descending turns on instruments are handled in much the same manner as in visual flight but the combination of changes in heading at the same time as alterations in height/altitude entails devoting more attention to the VSI during the scan (Fig. 5).

Climbing turns are used in most instrument procedures and both exercises are worthy of practice as a means of building up confidence and improving instrument flying skill.

SCAN: Check bank angle and nose attitude (AI). Check airspeed (ASI). Check rate of turn (Turn needle) and balance (Ball). Check rate of climb/descent (VSI) and correct with throttle as required. Check progress of the turn (DI) and start the roll-out 10°–15° before the new heading appears.

Transfer to Instruments after Take-off (climb established, full panel only)

Although holders of the IMC Rating may not take off when the visibility is less than 1 n.m. pilots with an Instrument Rating are often required to depart when the Runway Visual Range (RVR) is only 600 metres. When poor visibility is accompanied by a low cloudbase the pilot will be faced with the task of:

1. Maintaining direction along the runway when visual cues are not so easy to recognize.
2. Entering cloud soon afterwards and losing all outside visual references.

Maintaining Direction. It is essential to check that the DI is properly synchronized with the magnetic compass. To provide visual cues while accelerating down the runway it may help to position the aircraft slightly to the right of the centre line so that the markings can be seen from the left-hand seat.

During the early stages of take-off it is correct practice to check the engine instruments after the throttle has been fully opened. This is a good opportunity to quickly glance at the DI and confirm that the

Fig. 5   Instrument indications during a climbing turn (top picture) and a descending turn.

runway QDM is being maintained. However, when RVR is 1 n.m. or more it should not be difficult to maintain direction visually while still on the ground.

After leaving the runway visual cues may become obscured as height is gained. For example, 1 n.m. visibility along the runway will allow the pilot less forward view as the aircraft climbs and the 1 n.m. line of sight must be tilted to reach the ground (i.e. slant range). This is illustrated in Fig. 6.

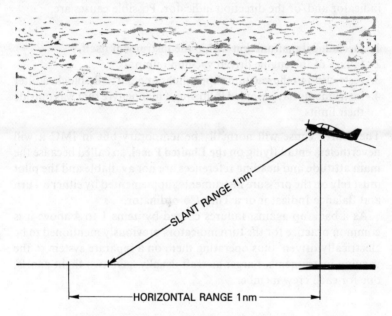

Fig. 6   The difference between Horizontal and Slant Range when visibility is limited, in this case, to 1 nm.

At a safe height and when well clear of all obstructions the pilot must transfer onto instruments *before* entering cloud. By adopting this procedure correct function of the flight panel will be confirmed while outside visual references are available should it be necessary to abandon the flight and return to the airfield. It is also good practice to be settled on instruments before entering cloud.

Having entered cloud all natural senses must be ignored and the instruments must be trusted implicitly.

Chapter 2
Flight with Partial Panel

For a variety of reasons it is possible to lose the use of the attitude indicator and/or the direction indicator. Possible causes are:

1. mechanical malfunction within the instrument itself
2. failure of the engine driven vacuum pump
3. restriction in the vacuum supply lines or a partially blocked filter
4. instruments have toppled following a manoeuvre that was outside their limits.

The fourth cause will normally be temporary but in IMC it will nevertheless entail flying on the **Limited Panel,** so called because the main attitude and heading references are not available and the pilot must rely on the pressure instruments supplemented by either a Turn and Balance Indicator or a Turn Co-ordinator.

As a back-up against failures caused by items 1 to 4 above it is common practice for the turn indicators previously mentioned to be electrically driven, thus operating them on a separate system to the vacuum instruments. Larger aircraft usually have two flight panels, one for each crew member.

Use of Limited Panel (no AI or DI information)

Prior to the early 1930s few aircraft were fitted with Artificial Horizons (as they were then called) yet instrument flying had by then become well established within both civil and military aviation. For example, RAF pilots in the late 1920s received instruction on taking off 'under the hood' (a folding roof which covered one cockpit but allowed the safety pilot unobscured vision) using a two-finger turn and balance indicator (known in those days as the turn and bank indicator), an ASI, a non-sensitive altimeter with a single finger and possibly two spirit levels of doubtful value. These were supposed to give an indication of lateral and pitch attitude during steady flight.

This small piece of history is intended to illustrate that instrument flying on the limited panel used to be regarded as normal before the war and the passing of time has not made it any less possible. However, the lack of pictorial information as displayed by the attitude indicator naturally makes the task more difficult than instrument flying with a full, Basic 'T' panel.

For the purpose of this chapter it is assumed that both the AI and the DI have become unserviceable and flight under IMC must continue with reference to the following instruments:

- airspeed indicator
- altimeter
- vertical speed indicator
- turn and balance indicator, or turn co-ordinator
- magnetic compass
- engine instruments.

Correct use of the trim control(s), always important even when flying visually, is vital to the success of flight on the limited panel.

Straight and Level Flight

It should be remembered that the ASI is a very accurate indicator of angle of attack. The VSI will provide climb and descent information which, even if the rates indicated are not particularly accurate, nevertheless presents valuable trend information, long term departures from the required height/altitude/flight level being shown on the altimeter.

Because of the close relationship between roll and yaw the turn indicator (i.e. the turn needle of a turn and balance indicator or the aircraft symbol in turn co-ordinators) provides good indications of lateral level and the ball will assist in maintaining balanced flight during the various manoeuvres.

Control in the Pitching Plane

To achieve level flight at a constant height/altitude/flight level the aircraft must be flown at the correct power setting for that airspeed.

Assuming the correct RPM have been set and the aircraft has been trimmed accurately at the correct IAS, height/altitude/flight level will be maintained. It should be remembered that, because of inertia, the aircraft cannot accelerate or decelerate instantly; however, the ASI will accurately indicate minor departures from fore and aft level.

The following instrument indications should be used while controlling the aircraft in the pitching plane:

Pitch change	Short-term indications	Long-term indications
Nose UP	ASI *reducing* VSI *climbing*	Altimeter *increasing*
Nose DOWN	ASI *increasing* VSI *descending*	Altimeter *decreasing*

Deliberate back and forth movements of the wheel/stick are rarely warranted during straight and level flight on instruments and, provided the correct power has been set and the aircraft is properly trimmed, all pitch corrections should be confined to small pressures.

Control in the Rolling Plane

The turn needle should be regarded as an indicator of lateral level and, provided the ball is not displaced from centre, the control wheel/stick should be moved away from the direction of turn to bring the needle/aircraft symbol back to its neutral (wings level) position. The gyro axis in a turn co-ordinator is tilted slightly and it is claimed that, as a result, bank indications are provided more readily than is the case with turn and balance indicators. The following instrument indications are provided on the limited panel:

Roll changes	Short-term indications	*Long-term indications
LEFT bank	Turn indicator *left*	Compass Hdg. *decreasing*
RIGHT bank	Turn indicator *right*	Compass Hdg. *increasing*

* Because of various turning errors (described later) departures from the required heading will only be accurately indicated after the magnetic compass has been allowed to settle with the aircraft at a wings-level, steady IAS.

Like the corrections in pitch, those for levelling the wings must be in the form of gentle pressures.

Control of Direction

Lateral stability is not powerful in most light aircraft of modern design, consequently it is important to keep the wings level if direction is to be maintained. The slightest bank will cause a turn and this should be remembered at all times, not only while flying on the limited panel.

Because the magnetic compass is subject to turning errors caused by acceleration and deceleration while flying on easterly/westerly headings and others resulting from slip/skid on northerly/southerly headings the instrument will only give meaningful heading indications when the aircraft is at a steady speed with its wings level. As a result the instrument is not ideal for maintaining heading.

Apart from the obvious need to keep the wings level maintaining a steady heading can be assisted by using the following technique:

1. The turn indicator has displaced from centre and is showing a left roll/yaw.
2. Gently apply sufficient opposite aileron to produce a turn indicator displacement to the right and hold it there for a period similar to the original displacement.
3. Roll the wings level with reference to the turn indicator.
4. At intervals, when the airspeed is steady and the aircraft is laterally level, check the magnetic compass and if necessary make gentle heading adjustments.

Control of Balance

During straight and level flight it should rarely be necessary to apply rudder inputs in single engine aircraft but this does not absolve the pilot from checking that the aircraft is in balance. Until experience has been gained flying on the limited panel can be a demanding exercise and it is easy for a pilot under pressure to apply rudder while under tension. In Chapter 1 the need to relax was mentioned. This is equally important when flying without a full instrument panel.

Out-of-balance corrections are confined to applying a little rudder pressure in the direction indicated by the balance indicator or, to quote an old flying instructor's saying – "kick the ball into the centre".

Control of Height/Altitude/Flight Level

Assuming the aircraft has been properly trimmed at the correct speed short-term departures from the required cruising level are usually caused by turbulence and these are best dealt with by lowering or raising the nose to regain height. A considerable height deviation, say 400 ft or more, will require an addition or reduction of power as the case may be.

A persistent gain of height when the airspeed is correct will be caused by too high a power setting and the method of adjustment is as follows:

1. The aircraft is gaining height at the required airspeed, indicating too much power.
2. Reduce power slightly, if necessary lower the nose and re-trim to maintain the correct speed.
3. Check lateral level and balance.
4. Check height and speed over a period and adjust as required.

Conversely, a persistent loss of height will require the following actions:

1. The aircraft is losing height at the required airspeed, indicating insufficient power.
2. Increase power slightly, if necessary raise the nose and re-trim to maintain the correct speed.
3. Check lateral level and balance.
4. Check height and speed over a period and adjust as required.

Having discussed the elements of straight and level flight on the limited panel it now remains to consider the exercise in total. It is very important to avoid over-correcting and to some extent this entails overcoming a psychological barrier: the inability to relax while flying on the limited panel.

Pilots who approach limited panel instrument flying with a degree of apprehension should always remember that all the information required for safe flight is available from the remaining instruments. Furthermore, turn indicators of all types have no toppling limits; in an extreme attitude the gyro, which is suspended in a single gymbal, comes up against its limit stops and immediately continues to provide proper readings when aircraft attitude returns to within the range of the instrument.

SCAN: Having set the correct power check fore and aft level (ASI and VSI). Check lateral level (Turn Indicator). Check height (VSI and

Altimeter). Check heading (Turn Indicator and Magnetic Compass). Check balance (Ball). Check engine RPM which, in aircraft with fixed pitch propellers, will be affected by changes in airspeed.

Climbing and Descending

The transition from level flight to the climb or descent must be made gradually, if necessary re-trimming in stages. Provided full use is made of the elevator trim control climbing and descending on the limited panel presents no special difficulties. However, unless the aircraft is fitted with an adjustable rudder trim considerable foot loads may be required to maintain balance during the climb at high power.

From Straight and Level Flight to the Climb

In some aircraft application of climbing power will itself cause a nose-up trim and often only minor trim adjustments will be necessary to hold the new speed. Entry to the climb is made as follows:

1. From straight and level flight open the throttle to the correct climbing power.
2. Keep the wings level and be prepared for torque and slipstream effect which will disturb balance. When the propeller rotates clockwise (as seen from the cabin) right rudder will be required to centre the ball. This will become more pronounced as speed is reduced for the climb. During a prolonged climb a deliberate effort will be required to maintain balanced flight.
3. Apply back pressure on the wheel/stick to attain the required climbing speed. This should be done in stages, re-trimming at intervals.
4. At the correct climbing speed check the trim and note rate of climb on the VSI.
5. Check lateral level and balance at intervals.
6. Before checking that the heading is correct on the magnetic compass it is *essential* that the airspeed is steady and the aircraft is in balance.

Returning to Straight and Level Flight from the Climb

Some pilots talk of starting the transition from climb to straight and level flight before the new altitude is reached. While this is necessary in high performance aircraft the technique usually results in levelling off at too low an altitude in light aircraft of low power. Better results will be obtained by levelling out at the new altitude. Sequence of events is as follows:

1. At the correct altitude progressively ease forward on the wheel/stick and allow the airspeed to increase. It may help to do this in stages, re-trimming at intervals. Do not reduce power at this stage.
2. Be prepared to reduce rudder pressure as speed increases.
3. Check that the wings are level and the aircraft is in balance.
4. At the correct speed bring back the throttle to cruising power.
5. Before checking the heading on the magnetic compass it is essential that the airspeed is steady and the aircraft is in balance.

From Straight and Level Flight to the Descent

When power is reduced to initiate a descent most aircraft of modern design automatically lower the nose and only minor trim adjustments will be necessary.

For changes in height/altitude/flight level it is normal practice to hold the present speed and reduce power according to the rate of descent required. Because of icing risk, reduction in electric supply and loss of slipstream over the tail surfaces gliding descents should not be practised while flying on instruments.

The Instrument Approach

When the descent is part of a landing approach additional factors are involved:

(a) Speed must be reduced.
(b) Approach flap will be lowered.
(c) The descent must be flown at a specific rate.

The transition from straight and level to descending flight is a straightforward one of reducing power, keeping the wings level, maintaining balanced flight and checking the trim. Flying the approach is slightly more complex and this is now described:

1. From straight and level flight move back the throttle and set the engine RPM at a figure known to produce the required rate of descent. Maintain balance with correct use of rudder.
2. Do not allow the nose to drop immediately but apply gentle back pressure on the wheel/stick. The aim should be to maintain height at this stage, a technique that will reduce airspeed. Re-trim in stages.

3. Check that the ASI is within the white arc then lower flap in stages, re-trimming at intervals.
4. Keep the wings level and maintain balance. Check the heading on the magnetic compass.
5. Make fine adjustments to the airspeed and check the rate of descent. If it is too high add a little power and if necessary re-trim at the correct speed. To increase the rate of descent reduce power slightly, check the airspeed is correct and if necessary re-trim.
6. At intervals apply *full* carburettor heat for a few seconds (or as recommended in the aircraft manual).

The instrument scan is the same for the climb and descent:

SCAN: Check the airspeed (ASI). Check the wings are level (Turn Indicator). Check balance (Ball). Check rate of climb/descent (VSI). Check height/altitude/flight level (Altimeter). Check engine instruments for correct RPM, temperatures and pressures.

Turning

The turn is, in itself, an easy to perform manoeuvre on the limited panel but adopting a new heading by using the magnetic compass for reference is certainly more difficult than using the gyro-operated direction indicator.

Entry to the turn is made by applying bank in the required direction until the turn indicator is showing Rate 1 (or Rate $\frac{1}{2}$ if this is required). Some aircraft may need a small amount of rudder in the same direction to maintain balance although generally modern designs will turn accurately on the ailerons alone. Here is the procedure to adopt:

1. Roll on bank in the required direction of turn. If necessary apply a little rudder in the same direction to maintain balance.
2. A tendency to lose height, which will be indicated by the VSI and the altimeter, must be prevented by gentle back pressure on the wheel/stick.
3. When Rate 1 (or if required Rate $\frac{1}{2}$) is indicated on the turn indicator return the wheel/stick to the ailerons neutral position to prevent over-banking.
4. Adjust turn rate by altering angle of bank and prevent a climb or descent with the elevators.
5. To roll out of the turn apply aileron in the opposite direction, maintain balance with the rudder and relax back pressure on the

wheel/stick to prevent a climb as the wings become level.

6. The wings level attitude will be indicated when the turn indicator is neutral and the ball is in the centre.

7. Check that the aircraft is neither climbing nor descending.

Compass Turns

On pages 47 to 50 of *Flight Briefing for Pilots* Vol. 2 the magnetic compass is described along with its various errors. The Earth's magnetic field tends to pull down the north-seeking end of the compass system while flying in the northern hemisphere and the south-seeking end in the southern hemisphere (a force known as Dip). Consequently, the instrument will only provide accurate readings when its magnet system is not tilted in a direction that will allow dip to distort its readings.

The magnetic compass will have been explained during the PPL Course and this section is a reminder of how it should be used in the air. The following rules relate to flights in the northern hemisphere:

1. Limit turns to Rate 1. Beyond that rate the compass becomes erratic and unreadable.

2. While turning onto east or west from a northerly or southerly heading roll out 10° before reaching the required compass heading. This will allow time for the turn to stop.

3. When turning onto north from an easterly or westerly heading roll out of the turn 20–25° before reaching the required compass heading. As the wings roll level the compass will swing through the last 20–25°.

4. When turning onto south from an easterly or westerly heading roll out of the turn 20–25° after reaching the required compass heading. As the wings roll level the compass will swing back through 20–25°.

5. While flying on easterly or westerly headings an acceleration will cause the compass to read an apparent turn towards north. A deceleration will result in an apparent turn towards south.

In the southern hemisphere items 3 and 4 are reversed, i.e. overshoot on north and undershoot on south.

Timed Turns

An alternative to relying on the compass while turning through a particular number of degrees is to attain a Rate 1 indication and use the stopwatch, allowing 3° per second. For example, a heading change from 045° to 075° would entail a right turn through 30° which, at Rate 1, translates into 10 seconds. Timed turns are made in the following manner:

1. Convert the number of degrees heading change into seconds, allowing 3° per second at Rate 1.
2. Roll into the turn in the normal manner, at the same time starting the watch.
3. Carry out the usual instrument scan.
4. After the calculated number of seconds roll out of the turn in the normal way.
5. When the aircraft has settled into straight and level flight check the heading with the compass and, if necessary, make minor adjustments.

Note that timing starts with the roll-in and the roll-out is commenced at the end of the count. Time required to start the turn is compensated for by time taken to roll wings level.

Provided an accurate Rate 1 turn is made it is possible to roll out within a few degrees of the new heading by using the timed turn method. The ability to count seconds accurately dispenses with the need of referring to the stopwatch.

The following scan will be used while making timed turns on the limited panel:

SCAN: Check stopwatch is running. Check rate of turn (Turn Indicator). Check balance (Ball). Check steady height (Altimeter). Check airspeed (ASI). Check stopwatch and after the calculated number of seconds roll out of the turn. Check compass and make minor heading adjustments. Continue straight and level checks.

Recovery From Unusual Attitudes

Loss of indications from the AI and DI could have been caused by allowing the aircraft to attain an attitude which is beyond the toppling limits of these two instruments. The direction indicator can easily be caged and re-set by using the synchronizing knob provided but 10 minutes or more may elapse before the Attitude Indicator's pendulous unit will have returned the instrument to normal.

Unusual Attitudes is the term used to cover any of the following situations. In practice they may occur in a variety of attitude combinations:

2 Flight with Partial Panel

1. Nose-high pitch attitudes
2. Steep angles of descent
3. Steep angles of bank
4. Spiral dives and spins.

Nose-high Pitch Attitudes and the Approach to the Stall

If a nose-high situation is allowed to develop there is obviously a risk of stalling. Without the benefit of an AI many pilots are unable to correct a steep nose-up/nose-down situation yet the ASI will provide clear indications when the nose is on or near the horizon. The following procedure should be read in conjunction with Fig. 7:

1. There is a rapid decrease in IAS, the VSI is showing a high rate of climb and the altimeter is indicating a faster than usual gain in height. It is obvious there is a nose-high attitude. The turn and balance indicator/turn co-ordinator is showing no turn or out of balance indications.
2. The throttle should be left in its present position while the wheel/stick is progressively eased forward.
3. Immediately the ASI stops decreasing and begins to move back towards normal cruising speed the nose is on or near the horizon.
4. Hold the attitude and allow the speed to increase.
5. Check heading, safety height, lateral level and balance. Re-trim if that was the cause of entering a nose-high attitude.

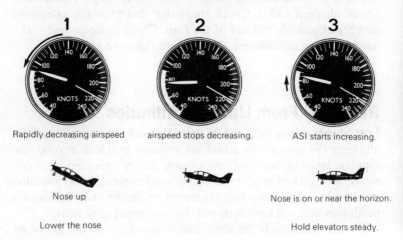

1	2	3
Rapidly decreasing airspeed	airspeed stops decreasing.	ASI starts increasing.
Nose up		Nose is on or near the horizon.
Lower the nose		Hold elevators steady.

Fig. 7   Recovery from a steep nose-up attitude
using the Limited Panel.

Approach to the stall

Recovery from an incipient stall is much the same as that just described but if the stall is entered it will be necessary to lower the nose more deliberately, at the same time adding power.

During the recovery lateral level and balance must be monitored and if the aircraft has entered a dive this should be dealt with in the manner now described.

Steep Angles of Descent

The following procedure should be read in conjunction with Fig. 8:

1. For some reason the aircraft has departed from straight and level flight. Although there are no turn/out-of-balance indications the airspeed is rapidly increasing, the VSI is showing a high rate of descent and the altimeter is winding down. Clearly the aircraft is in a dive.
2. The throttle is left in its present position as the wheel/stick is moved progressively backwards.
3. Immediately the ASI stops increasing and begins moving back towards normal cruising the nose is on or near the horizon.
4. Hold the attitude and allow the airspeed to decrease.
5. Check heading, safety height, lateral level and balance. Re-trim if that was the cause of entering a nose-down attitude.

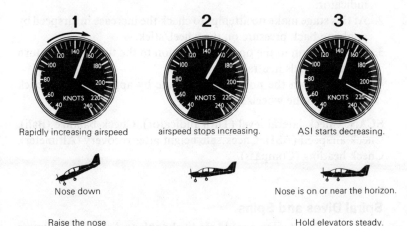

Fig. 8   Recovery from a steep nose-down attitude using the Limited Panel.

In each case, nose-high or nose-low, the point at which the ASI needle reverses direction and moves towards cruising speed signals that the nose is within a few degrees of the straight and level attitude relative to the horizon.

Steep Angles of Bank

Bearing in mind that turns on instruments, even when flying with a full panel, are limited to Rate 1 or less, an aircraft should not enter a steeply banked attitude intentionally. It will be remembered that in a steep turn considerable back pressure on the wheel/stick is required to prevent the nose dropping below the horizon. If the situation is allowed to develop a spiral dive will result when attempts to raise the nose with the elevators will have the effect of tightening the spiral.

When a steep bank occurs while flying on the limited panel instrument indications will include a high rate of turn when a turn and balance indicator is fitted. A weakness of turn co-ordinators is that they are usually incapable of indicating more than a Rate 1 turn with any degree of accuracy but such instruments will show more than Rate 1 in a steeply banked attitude. There will also be a loss of height and an increase in airspeed.

If a spiral dive is to be avoided prompt recovery action is essential. It may be effected in the following manner:

1. Determine the direction of bank with reference to the turn indicator.
2. At this stage make no attempt to check the increase in airspeed by applying back pressure on the wheel/stick.
3. Apply aileron in the opposite direction to the turn until the turn indicator reads neutral.
4. Recover from the nose-down attitude by applying gentle back pressure to the wheel/stick.

SCAN: Check lateral level (Turn Indicator). Check balance (Ball). Check airspeed (ASI). Check safe height after recovery (Altimeter). Check heading (Compass).

Spiral Dives and Spins

It is essential that pilots should readily be able to distinguish between the spiral dive and the spin because the two recovery actions are totally different. Instrument indications for the two manoeuvres are:

Spin indications	Instrument	Spiral dive indications
Low speed, fluctuating	ASI	High speed, increasing
Rapid height loss	Altimeter	Rapid height loss
High rate descent	VSI	High rate descent
Max. rate of turn	Turn indicator	Max. rate of turn
Opposite skid	Ball	No slip or skid

The comparison of instrument indications just described is illustrated in Fig. 9.

In each case the prime danger is rapid loss of height and this must be checked without delay. During a spiral dive there is the additional hazard of a fast increasing airspeed which could, if not checked, quickly exceed the aircraft's V_{ne} (Never Exceed Speed). Although on the face of it the only major difference between a spin and a spiral dive would appear to be one of airspeed the two manoeuvres are, in fact, totally different and the recovery action should be clearly understood because that for the spiral dive will not deal with a spin and *vice versa*.

Recovering from a Spiral Dive

1. With reference to the turn indicator determine the direction of spiral and apply bank opposite to needle/aircraft symbol indication.
2. Ease out of the dive and reduce power only if there is a risk of exceeding maximum RPM/V_{ne}.
3. When the ASI stops increasing and the needle starts to move towards cruising speed the nose is on or near the horizon. Check the altimeter and start an immediate climb when there is any danger of flying into the ground.
4. At a safe height the usual steps may then be taken to resume straight and level flight.

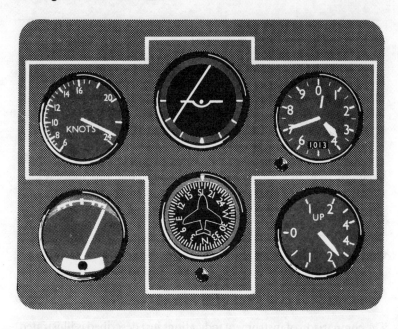

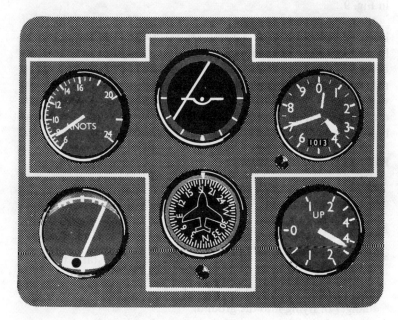

Fig. 9 Spiral Dive (top drawing) compared with a Spin
when seen on instruments.

Recovery from a Spin

1. When a spin has been recognized close the throttle, check the ailerons are neutral and at the same time determine the direction of spin with reference to the Turn Indicator.
2. Apply and hold on *FULL* rudder in the opposite direction to that shown on the Turn Indicator.
3. Progressively ease forward the wheel/stick until the turn indicator flicks to a maximum rate turn in the opposite direction and then centres. At that point the spin has stopped and rudder must be centralized immediately.
4. Allow the airspeed to increase but at the same time add power and ease back on the wheel/stick.
5. If necessary level the wings with reference to the turn indicator and check the ball for balance.
6. When the ASI stops increasing and the needle begins to move towards cruising speed the nose is on or near the horizon.
7. Check the altimeter and if there is a risk of flying into the ground establish a climb immediately.
8. At a safe height the usual steps may be taken to resume straight and level flight.

Pilots are often left with a strong impression that the aircraft is rotating in the opposite direction after recovery from a spin or a spiral dive. Clearly this is a time to ignore the natural senses and concentrate on the instruments.

Flight With Partial Panel, Loss of Pressure Instruments

So far this chapter has dealt with loss of the AI and DI. Another partial instrument loss that should be understood concerns the ASI, altimeter and VSI, i.e. the pressure-operated instruments.

The *Pitot and Pressure Head/Static System* is explained on pages 258 and 259 of Volume 2 in this series. When the pressure and static sources become blocked all three pressure-operated instruments will cease to function but in some cases emergency action can be taken to restore the situation.

Causes of Blockage

A pitot/pressure head cover should always be used while the aircraft is standing on the ground for any length of time since this will prevent the intrusion of insects, foreign particles, etc. Another possible cause of blockage is moisture and some aircraft are fitted with a drain valve.

In the air ice can block the pitot/pressure head and the effect of this on the instruments will vary according to which type of head is used.

Recognition of Pitot/Static Loss and Actions to be Taken

Pitot Ice will affect both the pressure and static lines since the two air samples are collected from a single probe which has an open end for obtaining pressure, surrounded by a static chamber which has slots cut into its sides. While the ice is blocking the pitot head the VSI and Altimeter have been known to indicate a loss of height although the airspeed, by now frozen at the last reading obtained by air samples before icing, appears normal. Such a situation will naturally induce the pilot to hold up the nose in an effort to stop the descent. In the absence of ASI readings this could lead to a stall on instruments.

A build-up of ice will affect all three pressure instruments. Initially they may act slowly or give erratic indications and this should be regarded as a warning of impending instrument failure, the most likely indications being:

(*a*) ASI reading zero or locked at one reading
(*b*) VSI locked at one reading
(*c*) Altimeter locked at one reading.

Pressure Head Ice. Because the probe is confined to obtaining samples of pressure air while a separate fuselage-mounted static vent (or vents) deals with static air supply, ice formation, when it affects such a system, can result in more complex misreadings. ASI readings will be distorted while the ice is forming until the following indications are given:

(*a*) ASI reading zero
(*b*) VSI operating
(*c*) Altimeter operating.

The foregoing notes should be regarded as no more than a guide because instrument misreadings can differ from one type of installation to another.

Dealing with Loss of the Pressure-operated Instruments

These days most light aircraft are fitted with an electrically-operated Pitot or Pressure Head heater and larger aircraft have similar ice protection for the static vents. Clearly prevention is better than cure and when there is the slightest possibility of encountering airframe icing, however remote, the heater should be switched on early in the flight.

If ice has been allowed to form more than a minute may pass before the heater is able to clear the blockage. During that time it will be necessary to fly the aircraft without the use of its ASI in the case of a pressure head + static vent installation. When a pitot head is fitted (i.e. a combined pressure/static probe) the flight will have to continue without use of the ASI, VSI and altimeter until the ice has been cleared.

To cater for possible loss of static pressure it is common practice to fit an alternative static source valve which is usually located within easy reach of the pilot. This will restore VSI and altimeter readings when, for any reason, static supply has become restricted. However, since cabin pressure may differ slightly from that outside the aircraft altimeter accuracy will suffer. Some aircraft are provided with a correction table for use when the alternative static source is in use.

Flying on Instruments when the ASI is Inoperative

Assuming the other instruments are operating, instrument flight without ASI indications should be conducted as follows:

1. Fly the aircraft on attitudes with reference to the AI. Provided the correct power is set for normal cruising speed and a steady height/altitude/flight level is being maintained, airspeed will be correct.
2. Prepare to land at the first airfield able to offer suitable facilities (e.g. radar, VDF, etc.).
3. For the descent reduce power to obtain the required VSI reading and if possible adopt a pitch attitude on the AI based on past experience. If unsure of the correct indication adhere to the straight and level picture and control descent rate on the throttle.
4. After breaking cloud known engine RPM, remembered from past experience, should be used during the approach. Provided the expected rate of descent is being indicated on the VSI, airspeed will be within a few knots of normal.

Conclusions

It would be misleading to claim that flight on the limited panel, due to loss of the AI and DI or loss of pressure-operated instruments, is an easy exercise. But the time may come when it is essential and obviously the pilot who has practised the various techniques described in this chapter will be better able to deal with the situation than one who deludes himself that 'it will never happen to me'.

The value of knowing approximate power settings for various phases of flight has been illustrated in this chapter. Such knowledge is of great value in reducing the workload while flying the various procedures on instruments.

Within the confines of its single flight panel the modern light aircraft is provided with a reasonable degree of instrument and system back-up but if full use is to be made of it pilots must accept the need for training.

Air Exercises — Applied Stage

Chapter 3

Radio Navigation and Instrument Approaches

The availability of lightweight avionics has transformed the capabilities of modern light aircraft. For example, when the Royal Air Force first introduced VHF transceivers at an early stage of the Second World War the equipment was limited to four frequencies selected on buttons A, B, C and D. The installation weighed approximately 35 lb and its transmitting power was limited to some 2½ watts.

By the early 1950s 36-channel equipment was in widespread use but it remained bulky and heavy. These days solid-state transceivers provide 720 channels, with a transmitter power of 7 to 10 watts or more for very low current consumptions, they often weigh 3 lb or less and the transmitter/receiver is no larger than a medium-size cigar box. Similar weight and space reductions (an important consideration in a small aircraft where all radio must be panel-mounted) have enhanced the design of all avionics, particularly equipment designed for use in light single- and twin-engine aircraft.

Weather Limitations and Aerodrome Operating Minima

Although private pilots are not subject to legal constraints which prevent their flying when the weather is below limits they have an obligation under the Air Navigation Order which requires them to be satisfied before take-off that the weather is suitable for the flight.

The somewhat vague nature of this arrangement often places the onus of decision upon those least equipped to assess the weather situation. Professional pilots, certainly those flying for an airline, will be subject to clearly defined rules which, among other instructions, prescribe the minimum weather conditions under which a take-off or landing may occur. Private pilots are, in this respect, largely left to fall back on their own judgement and this section is intended to provide guidance while explaining the concept of **Aerodrome Operating Minima**.

'Bad Weather' Definition

The following 'Bad Weather' definitions may exist in total or singly. Conditions slightly better than those listed should be regarded as on the limits of visual flight. In the take-off and landing context a cloud ceiling, in-flight visibililty or runway visual range/aerodrome visibility at or less than the figure listed will usually demand instrument flight:

Cloud ceiling: 1000 feet
In-flight visibility: 1 nautical mile
Runway visual range/aerodrome visibility: 1500 metres

Aerodrome operating minima factors of prime interest to the pilot are:

Take-off   Cloud ceiling
Aerodrome visibility/runway visual range

Landing   Decision height/minimum descent height
Aerodrome visibility/runway visual range
Visual references available for landing.

In these days of accurate approach aids the importance of airfield lighting should not be underestimated and the inter-relationship between radio and visual approach equipment will be described later in the chapter.

Radio Navigation

In the various exercises that follow this chapter use of the radio navigation equipment will be described. At this stage it should be understood that modern radio navigation is based upon two concepts:

1. **Point-to-point routes**. Usually the points, known as **Waypoints**, are marked by a radio facility suitably located on the ground although a waypoint may be determined by obtaining a fix from two facilities. A prime example of point-to-point navigation is the international airways system. Indeed, most of the radio navigation facilities are located within the airways.

2. **Area Navigation**. In some parts of the world, particularly over long stretches of water where no ground transmitters can be placed, larger aircraft navigate by inserting a series of waypoints into a

computer, usually in the form of a lat/long, and the equipment will then behave as though it were responding to ground stations. The equipment may be **VLF/Omega** (a VLF system which obtains accurate positions from a network of radio signals generated by eight phased transmitters located all over the world) or **Inertial** which is, in fact, not a radio aid.

Area navigation is achieved in light aircraft by electronically 'moving' a VOR/DME station to a more convenient position with the aid of a **Vector Computer**, sometimes known as a **Courseline Computer**.

The primary radio navigation aid is VOR/DME and although in some parts of the world ADF continues in widespread use, in the UK, most of Europe and the USA it is normally confined to acting as a locator beacon at the start of an ILS approach (described in Chapter 7).

Associated Charts

Since radio navigation is based upon fixing positions in relation to ground-based radio facilities, usually under IMC when map reading is not possible, purpose designed **Radio Navigation Charts** have been produced and these cover most areas of the world. These are described in Appendix II and part of a chart is shown in Fig. 10.

An alternative to the radio navigation chart is the standard topographical map which, these days, includes most of the radio facilities provided for navigational purposes. VOR stations are surrounded by a small compass rose to assist in transferring radials/QDM onto the map. A useful and inexpensive aid to this kind of navigation is the VORTRACK which is available at most flying equipment shops. It consists of bearing arms which may be attached to the map by inserting press studs through the VOR stations selected for the flight, adhesive compass roses and a parallel plate to assist in measuring off-radial tracks.

Instrument Take-off

Although many light, single-engine aircraft are fitted with comprehensive avionics and, in some cases, autopilots and flight directors, few have proper ice protection and the consequences of engine failure while flying in or above cloud while out of sight of the ground can obviously be serious.

Unless there is sufficient ceiling after breaking cloud, a forced descent, perhaps at a time when the terrain below is not known with

3 Radio Navigation and Instrument Approaches

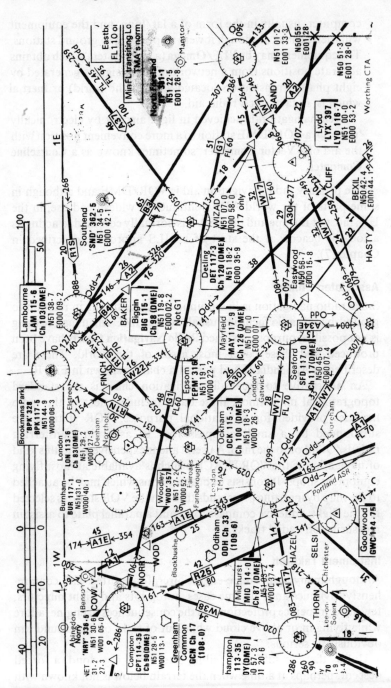

Fig. 10   Part of a typical Radio Navigation Chart (*by kind permission of AERAD*).

46

certainty, could entail the risk of flying into high ground or an obstacle, particularly when the problem is compounded by poor visibility. There is also the possibility that after take-off severe icing or a malfunction of some kind may dictate a return to the airfield. However, this would only be possible if the point of departure offered suitable weather conditions for a landing. These are matters to ponder and the advice that must follow is that even if you hold an IMC Rating:—

Never embark on a flight unless the weather is above the limits of the pilot AND THE AIRCRAFT.

Never take off unless the weather at the airfield, or a nearby alternate, is suitable for a landing.

Never embark on a flight under IMC before first checking the weather *en route*, at the destination and at the alternate(s).

Never commence a flight without full and proper flight planning, taking into account Notams, controlled airspace restrictions, the availability of radio aids and amount of fuel required for a diversion.

Never attempt to fly in IMC when you are not in instrument flying practice.

Never attempt to fly in IMC when the aircraft is an unfamiliar type.

Always file a flight plan in IMC, even when there is no legal requirement for you to do so.

Instrument Approaches

The instrument approach and landing should be considered in three phases:

1. Joining the approach aid;
2. Flying the procedure;
3. Transition from instrument approach to visual landing.

1. Joining the Approach

Probably the simplest method of aligning the aircraft with the extended runway centreline ready for an approach is by radar **Vectoring** (positioning). The method is in common use at busy airports where aircraft have to be sequenced to ensure a high landing rate while maintaining adequate traffic separation.

It is also usual to provide a low powered NDB (Non-Directional Beacon), suitably sited to guide aircraft onto an ILS approach. Such NDBs are known as **Locator Beacons**.

Whatever the type of approach it may be joined following a descent from cruising altitude or, when the destination is in an area of more intense air traffic, via a prescribed route with turning points usually marked by a radio facility. At one or more of these radio facilities (usually VOR or VOR/DME) there will be a holding pattern for use when approach to the airfield must be delayed because of heavy traffic. Such procedures are called **Standard Arrivals** and separate routes/patterns are usually prescribed to cover flights proceeding towards the airfield from different directions.

Associated Charts

For the main Terminal Areas (e.g. London TMA, Paris TMA, New York TMA, etc.) **Area Charts** are produced at a larger scale than Radio Nav Charts. Fig. 11 shows a section of the London Area Chart.

Instrument-rated pilots flying on airways will usually join the airport traffic by using Standard Approach Route (**STAR**) Chart(s). An example is shown in Fig. 12. Conversely, IMC-rated pilots will, when circumstances warrant, be given a **Special VFR Clearance** via specified **Entry/Exit Lanes** and to assist in complying with ATC instructions VFR charts are published for some airfields.

2. Flying the Procedure

Radio aids provided to guide an aircraft on the approach may either be **Precision** or **Non-precision**. The operating principles and aircraft/ ground equipment for these aids are described in Chapter 11. The approach aids most likely to be encountered by PPL/IMC qualified pilots and the chapters which explain their use in flight are:

Precision Aids

ILS (civil aviation)	Ch. 7
PAR (Precision Approach Radar, military aviation)	Ch. 8
Non-precision Aids	
VDF (VHF Direction Finding)	Ch. 4
VOR (sometimes with DME)	Ch. 5
ADF (Automatic Direction Finding)	Ch. 6
SRA (Surveillance Radar Approaches)	Ch. 8

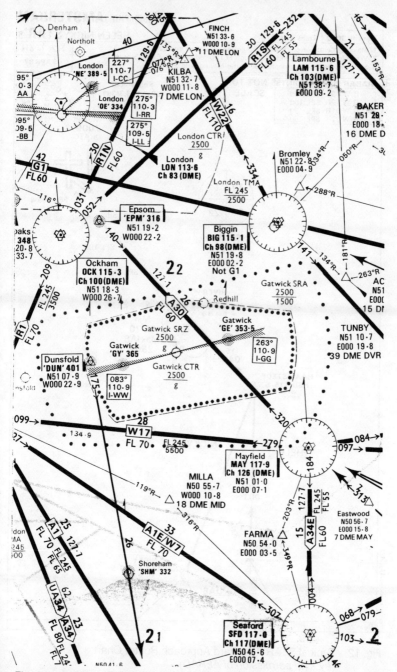

Fig. 11 Section of the London Area Chart (*by kind permission of AERAD*).

3 Radio Navigation and Instrument Approaches

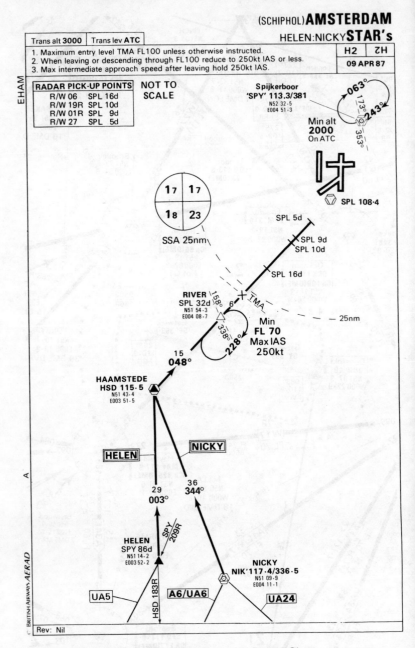

(SCHIPHOL) **AMSTERDAM**
HELEN:NICKY **STAR's**

Trans alt **3000**	Trans lev **ATC**

1. Maximum entry level TMA FL100 unless otherwise instructed.
2. When leaving or descending through FL100 reduce to 250kt IAS or less.
3. Max intermediate approach speed after leaving hold 250kt IAS.

H2	ZH
09 APR 87	

EHAM

RADAR PICK-UP POINTS	
R/W 06	SPL 16d
R/W 19R	SPL 10d
R/W 01R	SPL 9d
R/W 27	SPL 5d

NOT TO SCALE

Spijkerboor
'SPY' 113.3/381
N52 32·5
E004 51·3

063°
173°
243°
353°
290°

Min alt **2000** On ATC

SPL 108·4

SPL 5d
SPL 9d
SPL 10d
SPL 16d

| 1 7 | 1 7 |
| 1 8 | 23 |

SSA 25nm

RIVER
SPL 32d
N51 54·3
E004 08·7

158°
6
338°
228°

TMA
Min **FL 70** Max IAS 250kt

— 25nm

15 **048°**

HAAMSTEDE
HSD 115·5
N51 43·4
E003 51·5

HELEN   NICKY

29 **003°**   36 **344°**

HELEN
SPY 86d
N51 14·2
E003 52·2

SPY 209R

HSD 183R

NICKY
NIK 117·4/336·5
N51 09·9
E004 11·1

UA5   A6/UA6   UA24

BRITISH AIRWAYS AERAD

Rev: Nil

Fig. 12   Typical STAR (Standard Approach Route) Chart
(*by kind permission of AERAD*).

50

Techniques to be adopted while flying an approach using one of the aids listed above are explained in the chapters shown. However, certain considerations apply to all radio approaches, whatever the type of aid, and these are now explained.

Decision Height Calculation

Some modern transport aircraft are fitted with **Autoland**, a complex system based on two or three autopilots which receive instructions from the ILS transmitters and, in the final stages, the radio altimeter. Such equipment will safely land an aircraft in 'Zero-Zero' conditions (i.e. zero cloud base and zero visibility).

Light aircraft, even those with an autopilot, do not have Autoland capabilities and at some point on the approach it will be necessary for the pilot to concentrate on visual references so that a landing can be made. The lowest point at which transition from instrument to visual flight may be made is quoted as a height (QFE) or an altitude (QNH) and it is affected by these factors:

1. Obstacles on the approach and within the missed approach area;
2. Accuracy of the approach aid being used.

Designers of instrument approaches must obviously take into account the accuracy of the approach aid to be used. ILS and, at military airfields, PAR are the most accurate approach aids but others (e.g. ADF, VOR, etc.) are not capable of confining an aircraft to the same limits left and right of the extended runway centreline.

For purpose of design all obstacles on the approach, on each side and in the missed approach area, are taken into account. An imaginary slipway, clearing all obstacles and angled towards the runway threshold, is constructed and a similar surface, climbing away from the runway, is designed in the missed approach area. Often sloping sides are added to provide safe clearance from obstacles on either side of an accurate approach.

To ensure safe obstacle clearance during the transition from approach to missed approach a **Transitional Surface** is constructed. A typical **Precision Approach Obstacle Surface** is shown in Fig. 13.

Non-precision Approaches

When, for any reason, an ILS installation is operating without its glidepath transmitter it becomes a non-precision aid although its accuracy is better than VDF, ADF, VOR or SRA (Surveillance Radar Approach) which terminates at two miles from touchdown.

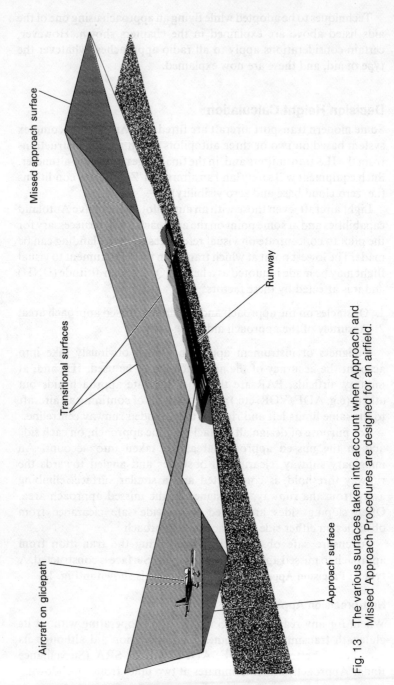

Fig. 13   The various surfaces taken into account when Approach and
Missed Approach Procedures are designed for an airfield.

When a precision approach aid is being used (ILS or, at military airfields ILS or PAR) the glidepath information provided enables the pilot to fly towards the runway on a narrow, constantly descending path. Non-precision aids provide no glidepath information and it is then necessary for the pilot to calculate rate of descent from a known position, usually a radio facility located on the airfield or on the approach.

Alternatively the pilot may elect to descend to the minimum safe height for that section of the approach and then fly level until a visual cue appears. When adopting this technique it is essential to guard against the risks of flying out of the protected area and entering one where the decision height calculation might be insufficient for safe terrain clearance.

To avoid these risks it is important to time the approach and if satisfactory visual contact with the ground has not been established when, according to the watch, the runway threshold should have appeared, missed approach action must be taken immediately.

At airfields sited near high ground it is sometimes necessary to adopt a stepped approach technique, flying at minimum safe height

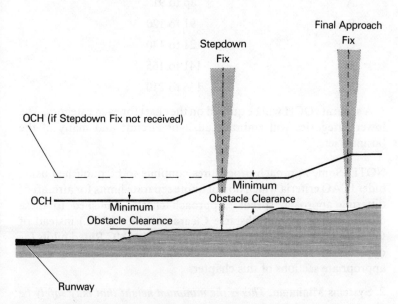

Fig. 14   The Stepped Approach, a procedure adopted when an airfield is situated near high ground.

until the next radio facility is overflown, thus signalling that another descent to the next minimum safe height may commence (Fig. 14)

The minimum height that will safely clear obstacles is known as **Obstacle Clearance Height, (OCH)** and the margin of safety built into these heights will depend upon the accuracy of the aid being used. **It should be clearly understood that any attempt to descend below OCH when visual contact has not been made could present high risks of flying into an obstacle**.

OCH does not allow for certain other factors which could erode safe clearance from obstacles. These are:

1. **Aircraft Category.** When a non-precision instrument approach brings the aircraft in sight of the airfield but not in line with the runway, bad weather **Circling** will be required to align it with the approach. Slow aircraft are capable of circling on a tighter radius than faster designs and these will sometimes have a lower OCH for any particular procedure. For this purpose, aircraft are divided into five performance categories:

Aircraft Category	Target Threshold Speed (knots)
A	up to 91
B	91 to 120
C	121 to 140
D	141 to 165
E	166 to 210

A separate OCH will be quoted on the chart for each category. The lower categories will embrace all light aircraft and many of the business jets.

NOTE: Some approach procedures continue to be published using older ICAO criteria which do not quote separate limits for aircraft of differing approach speeds. Approach charts published to these criteria will quote an **Obstacle Clearance Limit (OCL)** instead of OCH. Such minor differences as they apply to IMC Rated pilots (as opposed to Instrument Rated pilots) will be described in the appropriate sections of this chapter.

2. **Systems Minimum.** *This is the minimum height that may safely be flown on a particular approach aid. At present the following minimum figures are in use:*

Approach Aid	Minimum Height
ILS and PAR	200 feet
ILS (no glidepath)	250 feet
SRA (terminating at ½ n.m.)	250 feet
VOR	300 feet
ADF	300 feet
VDF (QGH or QDM procedure)	300 feet
SRA (terminating at 2 n.m.)	350 feet

3. **State Minima.** Some states, the UK is not one of them, publish minima. However many airfields do publish recommended minima for various classes of aircraft, according to their weight and whether they are propeller driven or jet.

Decision Height and Minimum Descent Height

Definitions of these two important terms are:

Decision Height (DH): The term relates to precision approaches and it is the lowest safe height to which the approach may be continued without establishing visual contact. It is measured relative to the runway threshold.

Minimum Descent Height (MDH): This term relates to non-precision approaches and it is the minimum height below which a further descent may not be made unless visual contact has been established. MDH also applies to bad weather circling when this is necessary to join the approach.

In determining DH or MDH the starting point is the highest of the height values quoted for items 1, 2 and 3 above. This will be shown on the approach chart as an OCH or an OCL. However, these heights take no account of pilot qualification or recent flying experience and the following safety margins should be added to obtain DH/MDH:

Instrument Rated Pilots in Current Practice

Precision Approaches: Take the OCH/OCL shown on the approach chart and add 50 ft to allow for altimeter correction.

Non-precision Approaches: Use the OCH/OCL shown on the approach chart. This has sufficient safety margin to ensure safe obstacle clearance.

IMC Rated Pilots in Current Practice

Precision Approaches: Add 200 ft to the DH/MDH for Instrument Rated pilots. Absolute minimum should be 500 ft.

Non-precision Approaches: Add 200 ft to the DH/MDH for Instrument Rated pilots. Absolute minimum should be 600 ft.

IMC Rated Pilots not in Current Practice

Pilots who have not flown for a number of weeks are strongly advised to avoid instrument approaches, particularly at strange airfields and when experience in the aircraft type is limited. If circumstances demand an instrument approach at least 100 ft should be added to the calculated DH/MDH figure for an IMC Rated pilot in practice.

Associated Charts

When an airfield has an approved instrument approach an **Approach Chart** (sometimes called an **Approach Plate**) will be published. At the larger airfields there will be an approach chart for each runway covering ILS, VOR, NDB or VDF procedures when one or more of these radio facilities are provided.

For the purpose of illustration AERAD charts are used in this manual. Generally the approach charts follow the same pattern irrespective of the radio aid upon which they are based. A typical example is shown in Fig. 15. The charts are divided into a heading section (airfield name, runway to which it applies and radio aid(s) depicted, airfield elevation, OCH/OCL, radio cummunication frequencies, chart number and its date). The main body of the chart is a plan showing the patterns to be flown, the airfield and high ground in various tints of green. The lower section shows the approach in elevation.

At the bottom of the chart is an instruction panel (centre) with time and descent rate panels for precision and non-precision approaches on each side. The various approach charts are described in greater detail in Chapters 4 to 8.

3. Transition from Instrument Approach to Visual Landing

At or before DH/MDH visual contact must be made if the procedure is to continue, otherwise missed approach action will have to be taken early enough to ensure that the aircraft does not descend below

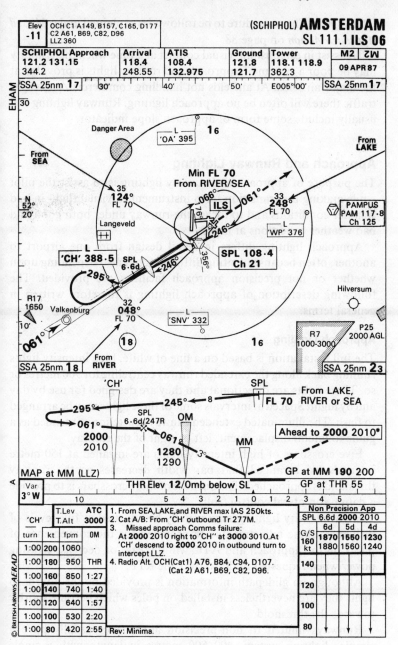

Fig. 15   ILS Approach Chart for Runway 06, Amsterdam
(*by kind permission of AERAD*).

OCH/OCL. The procedure to be followed is explained under *Missed Approach Action* on page 88.

To assist in establishing visual contact at a time when the visibility may be poor a system of approach and runway lights is provided at the major airfields. At airfields not handling commercial/passenger traffic there will often be no approach lighting. Runway lighting will usually include some form of approach slope indicator.

Approach and Runway Lighting

The purpose of approach and runway lighting is to assist the pilot while making the transition from instrument to visual flight in bad weather conditions and to locate the runway under both good and bad weather conditions at night.

Approach lighting differs in detail design from one airport to another, often because of siting difficulties but also depending upon whether or not precision approach facilities are provided. The following description of approach lighting is therefore written in general terms.

Approach Lighting

The full installation is based on a line of white, high intensity lights running back along the extended runway centreline for 900 metres or so. These lights are directional and they are designed for use by day and by night. Spaced at intervals some of these lights may be arranged to flash. The illuminated extended runway centreline is intended as a guide to lateral displacement, left or right of the runway.

Five crossbars of high intensity lights are installed at 150 metre intervals, so arranged that bar width decreases as the runway threshold is approached. The purpose of these crossbars is to provide a datum for lateral control (roll).

High intensity lighting may usually be adjusted at five levels of brilliance; these adjustments are provided for the convenience of pilots on the approach and ATC will increase or decrease lighting power when requested to do so over the RTF.

Although no glidepath information is provided by the approach lights they are nevertheless installed on poles which become shorter towards the threshold.

Runways limited to non-precision approaches usually have a simpler lighting system, 400–500 metres in length with a single crossbar located 300 metres from the runway threshold. Some installations consist of low intensity lighting of fixed brilliance.

Usually the lights are white and omni-directional but others are red and these are of limited use in daylight.

Approach lighting plays an important role in the final stages of a landing in bad weather and a long installation with powerful, high intensity lights can materially reduce the minimum safe visibility required to complete a landing following the transition from instruments to visual flight.

Approach Slope Indicators

Assuming the pilot has reached decision height and is satisfied that visual contact with the approach lighting is well enough established to continue towards the runway, glidepath information, previously provided by the ILS or by calculated rates of descent, will now have to be derived visually. Approach slope indicators are used for this purpose. The two most common systems are:

Visual Approach Slope Indicator (VASI).

A pair of illuminated bars, one upwind of the other, is positioned on each side of the runway threshold. The lights have built-in sectors, white when seen from above beam centre and red when viewed from below. The bar beams are directed back along the approach so that a pilot on the correct glidepath would see red bars in front followed by white bars behind. The display is repeated on each side of the runway.

If the approach is too high all bars will appear white and in an undershoot situation all bars will be red. This is illustrated in Fig. 16. During the transition from white to red or red to white a pink colour may appear. In bad weather the white lights are likely to be visible before red can be seen.

VASIs are generally regarded as reliable down to heights of 200 ft above the runway.

Precision Approach Path Indicators (PAPI)

Operating on a similar principle to that of the VASI from which it was developed this type of indicator consists of four light units positioned on each side of the runway threshold. The appearance of pink light during the transition from white to red or red to white has been more or less eliminated and standards of accuracy are such that reliable glidepath information can be provided down to 50 ft above the runway.

The various glidepath indications are illustrated in Fig. 17. but on a correct approach path (usually 3°) the two pairs of lights adjacent to

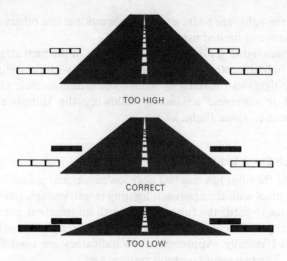

Fig. 16   Visual Approach Slope Indicators (VASI). Red lights are depicted as shaded in this illustration.

the runway will be red and the two outer pairs white. Some airfields may have variations of the systems described.

Runway Lighting

The outline of the runway (edges and ends) will be marked with lines

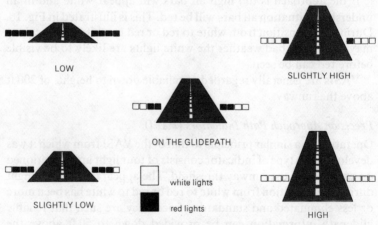

white lights
red lights

Fig. 17   Precision Approach Path Indicator (PAPI). Transition from white to red (depicted as shaded) is clear and without the pink light that occurs in most other systems. Accuracy at the runway threshold is claimed to be +/– 3 feet.

of lights, those across the start of the threshold usually being green. The threshold area is often marked with a distinctive pattern of lights and a series of flush lights may extend down the centreline, at intervals curving away as a guide to fast taxi-off exits which allow aircraft to clear the runway while still rolling at relatively high speed.

Visibility in the Final Approach Stages

It should be remembered that a pilot looking at the runway threshold during the approach has further to see than someone directly below the aircraft on the ground. Figure 18 shows that the higher the OCH/OCL for a particular approach the better must be the visibility if the runway threshold is to be seen when the transition is made from instrument to visual flight.

While the reverse may be the case under exceptional conditions visibility deterioration due to fog/haze, as measured from air to ground, tends to increase as height is gained. In other words, a pilot's slant visibility will usually be worse than that seen, for example, along the runway. Consequently reported airfield visibility will usually be better than conditions on the approach. However, **Runway Visual Range** is reported at some airfields and since this is assessed at a point five metres above runway centreline it is of more value to the pilot than airfield visibility.

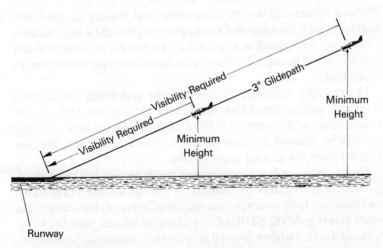

Fig. 18   The effect of OCH/OCL on minimum visibility required after the transition from Instruments to Visual Flight.

Final Stages of a Precision Instrument Approach

Ideally the sequence of events in an instrument approach flown at or near the limits should be as follows:

STAGE 1. At 50 ft or more above decision height at least two approach lighting crossbars should be visible. Roll and runway alignment corrections must be made immediately using the centreline and crossbars.

STAGE 2. As the aircraft descends more and more ground features should come into view over a wider area. If not, visibility conditions are such that it may be advisable to divert. When visibility is on the lower limits the ILS needle should briefly be checked to ensure that the aircraft is not above or below the glidepath.

STAGE 3. At 150 ft (QFE) the runway threshold should come into view and the touchdown area will be seen soon afterwards.

Ideally the aircraft should have been accurately established on the glidepath and on the centreline for the last 300 ft of the descent. However, when there is serious displacement to one side of the runway, or if the aircraft is very much above the glidepath, it may be necessary to execute missed approach action.

Final Stages of a Non-precision Approach

Without accurate glidepath information and bearing in mind that alignment with the extended runway centreline will be less accurate when using non-precision approach aids it follows that better visual conditions will be needed following the transition from instrument to visual flight.

For example, although VDF is a good **Cloud Break** aid the final stages of such a procedure may entail circling the airfield and positioning on the approach for a landing. At no time may the aircraft be allowed to descend below MDH (Minimum Descent Height) when the ground is not in view.

Under some conditions the ground might be seen but the runway could be obscured by poor visibility. A VDF procedure will be based on timed legs from overhead the station (Chapter 4) but some of the other aids (e.g. VOR, NDB) often include additional guidance in the form of DME suitably located to provide continuous 'distance to threshold' information. The various procedures are described in Chapters 4 to 8.

Forming a Mental Picture of the Approach

At first the approach charts will appear confusing because so much information is provided on a relatively small page. A good accountant develops the ability to locate immediately particular information from a balance sheet full of figures; likewise, a pilot who has practised reading approach charts can find whatever is required from the mass of information presented. Such practice can take place in the comfort of one's favourite armchair. It is certainly worth the time and effort.

Because of the mass of information presented it is essential to study all approach charts likely to be needed for the destination and alternates *before* the flight. Important information should be noted down. For example, an arrival in bad weather is no time to be looking for radio frequencies or checking the OCH/OCL for your aircraft and qualifications.

The joining procedure may entail special routings or, on occasions, a hold, and in the absence of radar vectoring the final turn may entail flying a **Teardrop** or a **Procedure Turn**. These are illustrated in Fig. 19. The location of the beacon in NDB approaches varies. At some airfields it is adjacent to the runway. At others it may be actually on

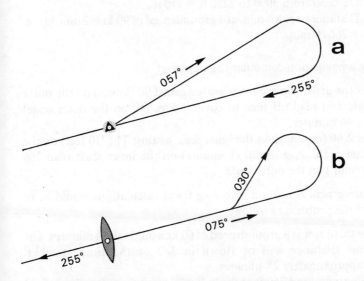

Fig. 19   Two methods used for reversing direction onto the final approach; (a) the Teardrop and (b) the Procedure Turn. According to the procedure, turns can be left or right hand.

the approach so that the beacon is overflown. Runway alignment then involves checking back bearings from the NDB and using the stopwatch to assess time to the threshold.

The descent could be at a steady rate or local terrain may require it to be stepped. Alternatively the procedure may entail using another radio aid to complement the approach facility (e.g. DME used in conjunction with ILS, VOR or NDB). Whatever the procedure it is essential to form a clear mental picture of the patterns to be flown. The approach chart to be used should be removed from the airways manual and clipped to the control wheel where it may be clearly seen along with the instruments. On no account should pilots attempt to fly with bulky manuals balanced on the knees while flying on instruments.

Calculating Descent Rates in the absence of Tables

Parts of most procedures, precision and non-precision, call for a descent through a certain number of feet over a particular distance. Rate of descent will naturally depend on groundspeed. Here are some examples:

> Descend from 3000 to 2290 ft = 710 ft.
> Distance to run 4 n.m. at a groundspeed of 90 kt = 2 min 40 sec.
> = 266 ft/min.

Using a navigation computer the steps are:

1. Set the arrow on the inner scale against 90 (knots) on the outer scale and read off time to cover 4 n.m. (40 on the outer scale) = 2.66 minutes.
2. Set 2.66 (minutes) on the inner scale against 71 (710 feet) on the outer scale. Against 10 (1 minute) on the inner scale read 266 (ft/min.) on the outer scale.

A more practical method involving fewer calculations would be to regard the problem as follows:

1. 4 n.m. to run at a groundspeed of 60 kt would take 4 minutes. The same distance will be flown in 2/3 of the time at 90 kt. = approximately 2½ minutes.
2. Aim to descend 360 ft at the half way point (i.e. after flying for 1 min. 15 sec. at 90 kt). If the aircraft has not arrived at 3000 — 360 = 2640 ft at the half-way point increase/decrease the rate of

descent for the second half **but do not descend below the prescribed 2290 ft**.

Flying a 3° Glidepath

The following table shows the rate of descent required to achieve a 3° glidepath at various groundspeeds. The figures have been rounded up for convenience:—

Groundspeed	Rate of Descent
60 kt	300 ft/min.
70 kt	350 ft/min.
80 kt	400 ft/min.
90 kt	450 ft/min.
100 kt	500 ft/min.
110 kt	550 ft/min.
120 kt	600 ft/min.

Time, Groundspeed and Drift Considerations

By now the importance of the watch will have become clear. It plays a vital part in the timing of such parts of the procedures as the outbound run from overhead the beacon to the turn and the inbound approach from the beacon to the runway threshold.

For the descent rates previously quoted to produce a 3° glidepath it follows that groundspeed must be known during the approach. This can be calculated by subtracting the wind reported by ATC from indicated airspeed, Usually a crosswind component on the approach will not be sufficient to affect the groundspeed calculation.

More complex are the distorting effects of a drift on the various patterns. The hold has already been mentioned and so have the procedure turn and the teardrop (see Fig. 19). In some cases wind effect can seriously distort these patterns to the point where the aircraft is incorrectly positioned for the next part of the procedure. Methods of dealing with drift are:

The Hold

In the UK more holds are flown right-hand than left. Methods of joining either pattern from different directions are illustrated in Fig. 20. A typical hold, showing the 'racetrack' pattern, is illustrated

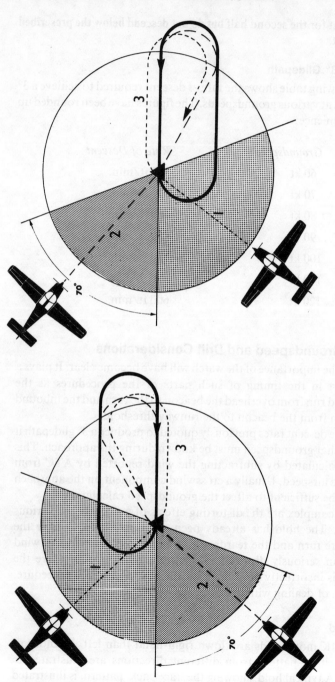

LEFT HAND PATTERN

RIGHT HAND PATTERN

Fig. 20 Method of joining a hold depends on the direction of approach to the radio facility.

in Fig. 21a. The leg flown towards the facility (NDB, VOR or VOR/DME position) is **Inbound** and the reciprocal leg flown after turning through 90° at Rate 1 is **Outbound**.

Fig. 21b shows the effects of a 30 kt wind from the left while flying towards the beacon:

1. The first turn from overhead the facility is of increased radius due to wind effect and the aircraft arrives at point **A** for the start of the outbound leg.
2. Drift during the outbound leg places the aircraft at point **B** where it will start the turn inbound.
3. Drift has the effect of decreasing the radius of the inbound turn, as a result the aircraft arrives at point **C**. In the case of an aircraft flying the hold at 180 kt the start of the inbound leg would be displaced by $1\frac{1}{2}$ n.m.

Compensating for Drift while Flying a Hold

For the purpose of simplicity it is assumed that the inbound and outbound headings are 090° and 270° respectively. Steps to be taken while dealing with a crosswind are illustrated in Fig. 21c.

1. Estimate the likely drift from the reported wind and check this while flying inbound towards the facility. In the example illustrated drift is 10° right and a heading of 080° is flown to compensate.
2. Start the turn outbound and be prepared to triple the drift allowance to allow for the following wind effects:
   (a) 10° to maintain 270° outbound.
   (b) 10° to regain $\frac{1}{2}$ n.m. drift at point A.
   (c) 10° to prevent $\frac{1}{2}$ n.m. drift that could occur while turning inbound from point B.

These steps should place the aircraft at point C ready for the next inbound leg.

Compensating for Head and Tailwinds while Flying a Hold

When the wind direction is in line with the axis of the hold its effects are less complex than in the crosswind case previously described. Nevertheless a strong head/tailwind can seriously distort the pattern if steps are not taken to compensate for wind effect.

Accurately flown a hold should take four minutes – one minute for the turn from the facility to outbound, one minute for the outbound leg, one minute for the turn inbound and one minute for the inbound

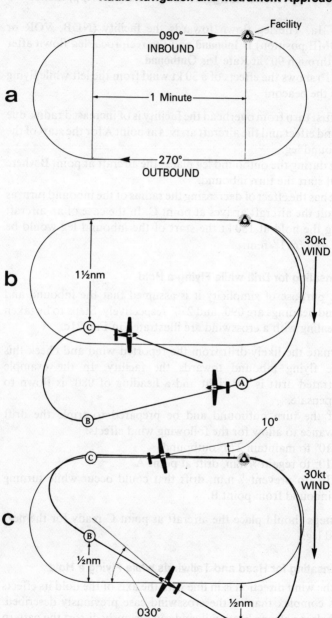

Fig. 21 (a) One-minute Racetrack Holding Pattern.
(b) Effects of wind without drift correction.
(c) Correcting for drift (see text).

leg. Of the various rule-of-thumb methods that have been devised to deal with this situation probably the simplest is as follows:

1. Allow 1 second per knot of wind.
2. Increase the into-wind leg by the number of seconds to be allowed.
3. Decrease the downwind leg by the number of seconds to be allowed.

Example

While flying the hold illustrated in Fig. 21a the reported wind for the level being flown is 090°/10 kt. There will be a headwind inbound and a tailwind outbound.

> 10 kt wind = 10 sec. allowance.
> Fly 1 min. 10 sec. inbound and 50 sec. outbound.

The Procedure Turn

Generally instrument approach procedures are based upon fixing the aircraft's position with certainty before various patterns are flown to place it on the glidepath. In the absence of radar vectoring this will often entail flying overhead a suitable beacon in the opposite direction to the runway QDM and at a prescribed altitude/height above the start of the approach.

The two methods of reversing direction from outbound to inbound are the procedure turn and the teardrop (which will be described later). Such patterns are necessary because a normal turn through 180° would place the aircraft perhaps 1 n.m. left or right of the extended runway centreline, according to the direction of the turn.

Fig. 22a shows a typical procedure turn (they can be left or right-hand). The first turn from outbound through 45° is followed by a 45-second leg. Some DIs have arrow marks around the dial at intervals of 45° and these are useful for determining the new heading without having to add or subtract 45 from the outbound heading. The final turn towards the extended runway centreline should place the aircraft on or near the approach.

Compensating for Drift while Flying a Procedure Turn

Usually the axis of a procedure turn will be the extended runway centreline so that the most usual wind effects will be those illustrated in Figs. 22b and 22c. These show the distortions to be expected while turning from downwind to into-wind (b) and from into-wind to downwind (c). Appropriate drift corrections of 10° to 20° according to wind strength should be made while flying the 45-second leg.

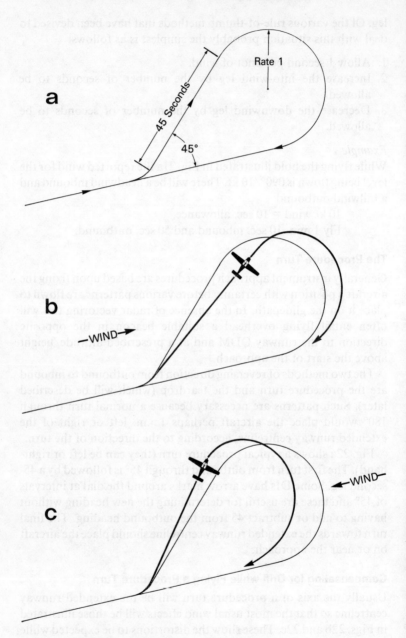

Fig. 22 (a) The Procedure Turn.
(b) Distorting effects of a tailwind.
(c) Distorting effects of a headwind.

The Teardrop

An alternative method of reversing direction during a procedure is the teardrop (sometimes called a **Butterfly** pattern). This is illustrated in Fig. 19 on page 63.

The outbound leg is flown at an angle of 10° to 20° or so from the extended runway centreline. At the end of the prescribed time, which will be shown on the approach chart, a turn onto the approach is made.

Compensating for Drift while Flying a Teardrop

This is a very simple pattern to fly and relatively easy to comply with in the presence of a crosswind because there are constant back bearings outbound. When there is a head or tailwind the 'one second per knot of wind' method described for the hold should be used.

Turning onto the Approach and the Importance of Lead

Progress must constantly be checked during the final turn because it may have been started too near or too far from the extended runway centreline, possibly because of wind effect or an inaccurately flown outbound leg/procedure turn.

Figure 23 illustrates two typical situations. When, for example, the

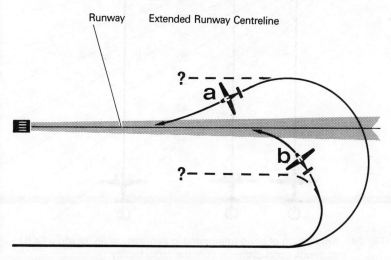

Fig. 23   Correcting faults while joining the extended runway centreline:
(a) Flying through the QDM.
(b) Undershooting the QDM.

aircraft has altered heading through 120° of the final turn and the radio instruments indicate that the turn will be completed before joining the required QDM (aircraft b) reduce the rate of turn or, in extreme cases, stop turning for a few seconds.

If the extended runway centreline is flown through before the aircraft is heading in the correct direction (a) continue turning, roll out on a heading converging 15° to 20° with the required QDM but be prepared to turn in the opposite direction as the extended runway centreline is regained.

To avoid the two situations just described pilots should develop the ability to anticipate the QDM/QDR being joined by allowing for the radius of turn. The technique of starting the turn before reaching the QDM/QDR is called **Lead** and the number of degrees anticipation will depend upon distance of the aircraft from the radio facility. This is illustrated in Fig. 24.

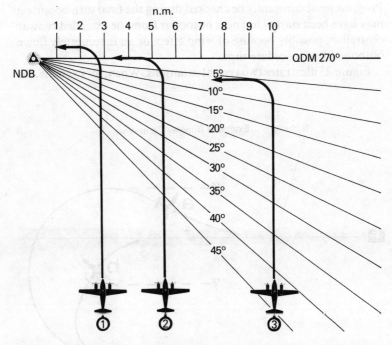

Fig. 24   Application of Lead (measured in degrees) while joining a QDM depends upon distance from the radio facility:
Aircraft 1 has turned too late (insufficient Lead).
Aircraft 2 has turned with correct Lead.
Aircraft 3 has turned too soon (too much Lead).

The various instrument indications presented by the radio aids are described in the chapters that follow.

Illusions affecting Visual Perception during a Landing Approach

The following conditions may on their own or in various combinations create a distorted impression of the approach. They may be regarded under two main headings:

1. Weather illusions
2. Terrain/airfield illusions

Weather Illusions

RAIN may reduce the intensity of approach and runway lighting and give the impression that the airfield is further away than reality. This is most likely to occur in heavy precipitation. Scattered droplets from lighter rain can act as minute lenses, magnifying some lights and having the effect of shortening apparent distance. Some angular distortion may also occur giving the impression that an approach is above or below the glidepath or to one side of the extended runway centreline.

Under some conditions a heavy rain storm has been known to create the illusion that the horizon has dropped below the nose. This will naturally encourage the pilot to move forward the wheel/stick and perhaps result in a shallow dive at a critical phase of the approach.

SHALLOW FOG, which may occur below decision height, can seriously reduce visibility during 'short finals' and the landing phase. When the fog has reduced RVR below the minimum recommended for the airfield (1 n.m. for an IMC Rated pilot) a diversion is strongly advised.

Terrain/Airfield Illusions

APPROACH TERRAIN sloping uphill towards the runway can give an impression of overshooting and higher ground below the aircraft that runs down towards the runway may create an illusion of undershooting.

A surprising factor is the potential danger of approaching over featureless ground/water. There may be no visual cues and even in good visibility an impression of being too high can encourage the pilot to adopt a high rate of descent. Even in daylight snow can totally destroy judgement of height during the final stages of an approach, the hold-off and landing. Further difficulties may also be caused when approaching into sun.

RUNWAY ILLUSIONS may take the form of imagining the available landing distance to be short because the runway is wider than usual and its edges appear to converge more sharply than expected. A wide runway can also give an impression of being lower than the actual height of the aircraft above the surface.

Runways that slope sufficiently to be appreciated from the air are uncommon but it should be remembered that the glidepath is intended to deliver an aircraft to the runway threshold and the ideal 3° is measured relative to the horizontal, not the runway surface. A runway that slopes uphill will give the impression that a steeper than usual approach path is being flown and the pilot will be induced to descend below the glidepath.

When the runway slopes downward an impression can be created that too shallow an approach is being flown and the pilot will naturally climb above the glidepath. These illusions can lead to incorrect use of power while on the approach.

All of the illusions described are best dealt with by checking visual cues at intervals with the flight and radio instruments until the actual landing which will be made visually.

Liaison with ATC

Services available to the pilot over the RTF naturally vary according to the size and importance of the airfield/airport. Each service usually operates on a separate frequency although some functions may be shared. Airfields will offer one or more of the following services. When making a radio call the service requested is preceded by the name of the airfield. e.g. **'Gatwick Approach'**.

GROUND	Control of aircraft while on the ground, start-up clearance, taxi instructions and general information.
TOWER	Departure and landing clearances and control of traffic within the airfield circuit, also ATC clearances. Some of the larger airports have a separate service, callsign **DELIVERY**, which handles clearances on a separate RTF frequency.

APPROACH   Control of aircraft and information for pilots joining, departing or overflying airfield traffic.

HOMER   VDF homer service.

RADAR   Radar vectoring and approaches.

INFORMATION   General off-airways information within a flight information region.

CONTROL   Services operated by an area control centre (ACC). These include airways control.

Additional to the civil ATC services described above are the military functions provided to ensure safe transit through the Military Aerodrome Traffic Zones (MATZ). When, as is often the case, a number of these airfields are in close proximity one of them will be designed as the **Master Station**, sometimes known as the **Clutch Controller**.

Division of Responsibilities

In essence the air traffic control system may be regarded as an aerial railway network with radio instead of visual signals. Unlike other vehicles an aircraft cannot stop although there must be many times when the air traffic control service wish it were possible to halt a particular echo on the screen so that other traffic could pass with an adequate margin of safety.

The aeronautical equivalent of stopping the train at a red signal is the hold. Aircraft may be 'stacked' at 1000 ft intervals over a hold when heavy traffic is causing arrival delays. As an approach becomes vacant the aircraft at the bottom of the stack will be cleared into the procedure and the others will usually be given permission to descend.

So that pilots may know when to expect release from the hold it is usual for ATC to give an **Estimated Approach Time (EAT)**.

It goes without saying that clear, unambiguous communications between ATC and pilot are vital to the success of an instrument flight. Examples are given in the chapters that now follow.

Chapter 4
VHF Direction Finding (VDF)

When operated at a civil airfield VDF is almost invariably used as a **Pilot-interpreted** aid; on request bearings are passed to the aircraft via RTF and the pilot must then interpret the information received in order to navigate or fly the procedure.

During the various procedures it may be of assistance to visualize the VDF station as the centre of 360 position lines, radiating outwards at intervals of 1 degree. For training purposes the easily made bearing chart illustrated in Fig. 25 will be of assistance. It should be placed within a plastic cover so that various procedures may be drawn and erased for repeated exercises.

The information provided by VDF is intermittent and it is therefore important that the pilot should, by intelligent interpretation of the readings passed from ground to air, form a mental picture of progress in relation to the airfield.

Establishing Communications with the Air Traffic Control Service

VDF may be used for the following purposes:

1. Establishing position lines along a track;
2. Tracking to or from a VDF station;
3. VDF Cloudbreak/VDF approach.

When one of these services is required an initial RTF call will be made to the VDF station thus:

(a) Station callsign (e.g. 'Shoreham Homer')
(b) Aircraft callsign.
(c) Present altitude/flight level.
(d) Approximate position.
(e) Service required (e.g. QDM, VDF letdown, etc.).

When a bearing is passed to an aircraft the VDF station will give the figure in degrees followed by Class 'A', 'B', or 'C' according to the

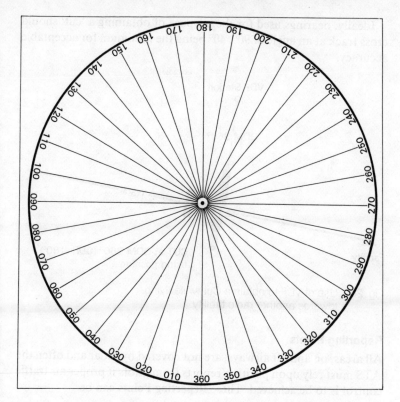

Fig. 25   A QDM Chart can be of assistance while under training.

quality of the reading. These are: Class A accurate within ± 2°

Class B accurate within ± 5°

Class C accurate within ± 10°

The various VDF procedures will now be described.

Use of VDF Bearings to Fix Position

Figure 26 shows a typical situation where the aircraft is tracking towards a VOR or an NDB. If the VOR station were co-related with a DME transmitter and the aircraft was fitted with DME a position could be obtained on a **Bearing and Distance** basis. However, in the case illustrated no DME is available and there are no other VOR or NDB transmitters conveniently placed to provide a **Cut**, i.e. a position found with the aid of bearings from two radio facilities or a radio facility and a ground feature (e.g. coastline, railway, etc.).

4 VHF Direction Finding (VDF)

Ideally, bearings used for the purpose of obtaining a 'cut' should cross track at an angle of 90°, 40° being the minimum for acceptable accuracy.

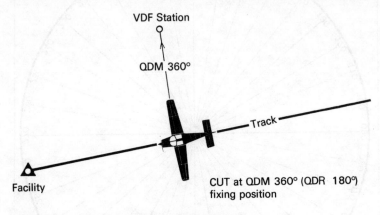

Fig. 26   Use of VDF to obtain a Cut while flying towards another radio facility.

Reporting Points

All areas, on and off airways, are not covered by radar and often the ATS must rely upon position reports from pilots if proper air traffic control is to be achieved. These **Reporting Points** can be:

Compulsory, shown on charts as a ▲
On Request, shown on charts as a △
Sector Point, shown on charts as a X

Although reporting points are often marked by a radio facility this is not always the case and it is then necessary to obtain a 'fix' in the form of a VOR/DME bearing and distance, a VOR/VOR cut, a VOR/NDB cut or a VDF cut. For operational purposes the airways are broken into sectors and these are demarked by the sector points mentioned above. Usually they must be located by obtaining a cut or a bearing and distance.

When during flight planning a reporting point is noticed and its location requires the use of a conveniently positioned VDF station the QDM (magnetic bearing) FROM the reporting point to the VDF station should be drawn on the map/chart and then measured for use in the air. In the example shown (Fig. 26) provided the aircraft is tracking correctly towards the radio facility it will be over the reporting point when the station reports 'QDM three six zero'.

Frequency of Bearing Requests

While the aircraft is some distance from the required QDM requests for bearings need only be made at intervals of 30 seconds or so (assuming light aircraft speeds). As the bearings reported become closer to that required bearings must be obtained more frequently. Because the VDF operator is presented with an instant reading transmissions need only be of short duration, e.g. 'Charlie Delta QDM'.

Use of Bearings to Assess Drift

Figure 27 illustrates a typical example of flying to a station on a particular QDM in the presence of drift. In this case the aircraft is on a heading of 045° and will soon intercept the required 360° magnetic track inbound to the airfield. The procedure would be as follows:

Aircraft:	'Walton Homer Golf Alpha Bravo Charlie Delta, Piper Navajo flight level four zero approaching from the south west, QDM, over.'
Walton Homer:	'Golf Charlie Delta QDM zero one zero, class Bravo.'

This indicates that the aircraft is almost due south of Walton Homer and the bearing obtained was accurate to within ±5°. The pilot would continue to obtain bearings until, shortly before the aircraft closes with QDM 360°, heading is altered from 045° to 360°.

As the aircraft tracks towards the homer the pilot must check for drift. In the example illustrated a series of reducing bearings confirms that the wind is from the left and there is drift to the right. The simple rule to remember is:

QDM decreasing, alter heading LEFT, wind from the LEFT.
QDM increasing, alter heading RIGHT, wind from the RIGHT.

By a process of trial and error the correct drift allowance can be found. This will be confirmed when a series of steady bearings have been received.

Use of Bearings to Assess Station Proximity

If bearings radiating from a VDF homer are imagined as the spokes of a bicycle wheel a little thought will reveal that rate of bearing change will become more rapid as the facility is neared. Naturally the

4 VHF Direction Finding (VDF)

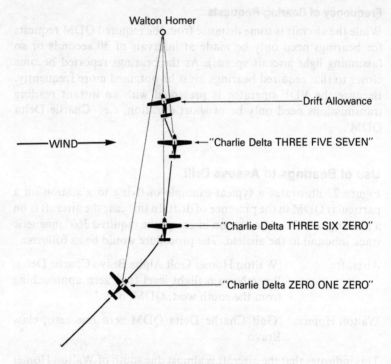

Fig. 27   Homing to the VDF station in the presence of drift.

most rapid QDM changes will occur when the aircraft is flying across the bearings while close to the VDF homer. The following procedure for calculating distance from the facility may be used with VOR, NDB or VDF.

1. While flying towards a VDF (or VOR/NDB) turn through 90° from the QDM being flown.
2. Obtain a series of bearings and time the number of seconds required for a 10° alteration in QDM.
3. Number of minutes required to overfly the VDF, VOR or NDB is found by taking 10 per cent of the number of seconds timed in stage 2.

The example illustrated in Fig. 28 shows that the procedure described is based on the 'one-in-sixty' rule. In this case the aircraft has a groundspeed of 120 kt and it has taken 5 minutes to fly through 10° of bearing changes.

5 x 60 = 300 seconds.

10% of 300 = 30 minutes to the facility.

PROOF: 30 minutes at 120 kt = 60 n.m.

10 n.m. at 60 n.m. from facility = 10° angle.

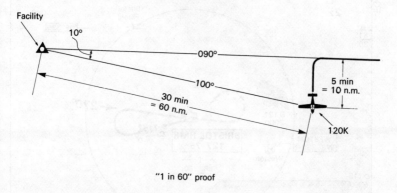

"1 in 60" proof

Fig. 28   Timing bearing changes to determine station proximity.

When bearing changes are particularly slow the same procedure may be speeded by timing through 5° of QDM change and doubling the number of seconds before taking 10 per cent to find number of minutes to overfly the facility.

The method described in this section should be regarded as an approximation since it takes no account of wind effect.

The VDF Let-down and Approach

Airfields offering VDF facilities will have a published procedure. A typical example is the BRISTOL AIRPORT VDF 27 approach chart which is reproduced on page 82. Study the chart and note:

1. Airfield elevation 620 ft.
2. OCH 570 ft. Decision height would be as follows:

   570 ft + 50 ft (for I/R pilots)   = 620 ft.

   + 200 ft for current IMC pilot   = 820 ft.
3. The radio frequencies for approach, radar and tower.
4. Date of chart which must be the latest published.
5. Sector safe altitudes shown in each corner of the plan section of the chart.

4 VHF Direction Finding (VDF)

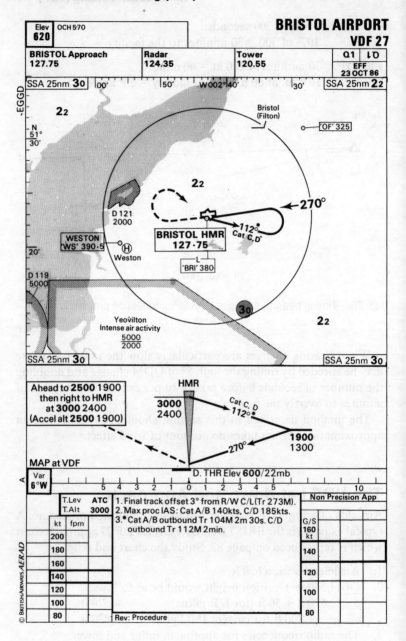

BRISTOL AIRPORT
VDF 27

| Elev **620** | OCH 570 | | | | Q1 | LO |

| BRISTOL Approach **127.75** | Radar **124.35** | Tower **120.55** | EFF 23 OCT 86 |

Ahead to **2500** 1900
then right to HMR
at **3000** 2400
(Accel alt **2500** 1900)

MAP at VDF

| Var 6°W | | | | | | | | D. THR Elev 600/22mb |

1. Final track offset 3° from R/W C/L (Tr 273M).
2. Max proc IAS: Cat A/B 140kts, C/D 185kts.
3.* Cat A/B outbound Tr 104M 2m 30s. C/D outbound Tr 112M 2min.

Non Precision App

	T.Lev T.Alt	ATC 3000		G/S 160 kt
kt	fpm			
200				140
180				
160				120
140				
120				100
100				
80				80
		Rev: Procedure		

© BRITISH AIRWAYS AERAD

6. Prohibited area D121 (not below 2000 ft) and the Yeovilton intense air activity area which is active between 2000 and 5000 ft.

7. Location of 'Bristol Homer' and its frequency (127.75).

8. The outbound track (M) shown as 112* which refers to Note 3 in the lower section of the chart. This requires that Cat A/B (slower) aircraft should fly a QDR of 104° for 2 min. 30 sec. before turning inbound. Faster (Cat.C/D), which will make a final turn on a larger radius, fly outbound on a QDR of 112° for 2 min.

9. The inbound track (M) of 270° which, according to Note 1 should be offset by 3° RIGHT on short finals. This is because the homer is located to the left of the runway.

10. The missed approach pattern printed in broken lines.

The Elevation Section shows the following information:

11. The aircraft must start the procedure by flying over the homer at 3000 ft QNH (2400 ft QFE).

12. While flying outbound a descent is made through 1100 ft over a period of 2.5 min. = 440 ft/min. At the end of this time the aircraft makes a level turn at 1900 ft QNH (1300 ft QFE) onto 270° inbound.

13. The scale shows 6 n.m. from the turn to the homer. Assuming a light aircraft being flown by an IMC rated pilot in current practice the 820 ft decision height will be reached 2½ miles from the Homer if a 3° glidepath is to be flown on the final approach (a table of heights v. distances to touchdown is on page 145). In this case 1300 – 820 = 480 ft must be lost over a distance of 3½ n.m.

14. The table on the right is left blank for the pilot to complete. Assuming an approach groundspeed of 80 kt the 3½ n.m. to Decision Height will take 2 min. 38 sec. so heights to attain at the end of each minute should be noted in the three spaces adjacent to the figure 80. With 480 ft to lose in that time a descent rate of 180 ft/min. would be used so the figures to write in would be 1120, 940 and 820 (decision height).

15. Note the missed approach procedure which entails maintaining decision height to overhead the facility then climbing straight ahead to 2500 ft QNH (1900 ft QFE) before turning right and flying to arrive overhead the homer at 3000 ft QNH (2400 ft QFE). At that point the pilot may elect to fly another approach or divert to another airfield.

At first approach charts may appear complex and confusing but in time one learns how to locate vital information instantly. However, with charts such as the example shown on page 82 it is important to calculate the approximate rate of descent for the final approach and write in the appropriate figures *before* the flight. Time spent on studying a variety of charts on the ground is an inexpensive and effective way of learning to read them as fluently as a book.

Station Transit (Overflying the Facility)

While flying towards Bristol Airport ATC will advise details of other traffic, airfield weather, runway in use, QNH and QFE. **QNH and QFE must be written down and read back**. The FREDA checks should be completed at this stage.

Imagine the aircraft is approaching Bristol Airport from the north-west. Ideally it should fly overhead the facility (Bristol Homer) so that a turn can easily be made onto the outbound heading of 104°(M) which is the QDR for aircraft flying at up to 140 kt. (Notes 2 and 3 in the chart panel).

The turn onto 104° from overhead the facility will, because of turning radius, fly the aircraft to the right of the required magnetic track and initially a heading estimated to close with 104° (taking into account wind conditions) should be flown until bearings received confirm interception of the outbound QDR. When there is little wind a heading of 090° would close with the QDR at an angle of 14°.

When experience of VDF has been gained a better method while approaching the airfield would be to position the aircraft slightly to the west of the airfield. As the aircraft flew nearer the homer bearings would rapidly change until 'QDM one one five' was passed to the pilot. At that stage a turn towards the airfield would be made in the knowledge that heading is within a few degrees of the outbound QDR.

Frequency of requests for bearings should at this stage be every 8–10 seconds (representing a distance of approximately a quarter of a mile) until Bristol Homer reports 'no bearing' at which point the aircraft is overhead the facility.

Use of QDMs to Establish and Maintain Outbound Heading +/– Drift

The outbound magnetic track which forms part of the teardrop turn shown on the BRISTOL AIRPORT VDF 27 chart is a QDR (magnetic heading to steer away from the station assuming conditions of no wind). Since VDF equipment may only be selected to indicate QDMs or QTEs (p. 194) VDF is an all-QDM procedure and the pilot must convert the outbound magnetic track by adding/subtracting 180°. Some VDF charts give both QDR and QDM but in this case the 104° outbound track (M) must be converted by adding 180° = 284°.

On overflying the homer the watch is started. It is to play an important role throughout the procedure that follows. While flying outbound for 2½ minutes the pre-landing checks must be completed and the following actions will be taken:

1. To lose 1100 ft in 2½ minutes rate of descent should be 440 ft/min. It is good practice to make a progress check at the half-way point; after 1 min. 15 sec. the aircraft should have descended from 2400 to 1850 ft. If the aircraft is too high or too low, descent rate will have to be adjusted but **on no account descend below 1300 ft QNH**.

2. Bearings obtained soon after overflying the homer are usually of little value – remember that near the station the bearings are closely spaced like the spokes of a cycle wheel. As distance between aircraft and homer increases so the bearings will be more meaningful and it will be possible to assess departures from magnetic track which may be caused by drift or inaccurate steering.

   When flying away from the station methods of correction are the reverse of when tracking towards the homer. They are nevertheless logical and simple to implement:

   turn LEFT to DECREASE and RIGHT to INCREASE QDMs

   which is the same as normal compass heading technique. In this case the required outbound track (M) is 284°. If after, say, one minute 'Bristol Homer' reports QDM two nine zero the aircraft is to the right of track and a 12° LEFT heading alteration onto 272° should correct the situation during the next minute. When 'QDM two eight four' is received heading should be altered to 278°.

3. A bearing request should be made just before 2½ minutes has elapsed to ensure that the final turn will be started from the correct position. If the aircraft is to the right of track (a bearing of more than 284° will confirm this) rate of turn should be decreased slightly. If the aircraft is to the left of track (indicated by a bearing of less than 284°) it will probably fly through the

extended runway centreline and this will have to be regained during the approach.

The Final Turn

4. At the end of the outbound leg the aircraft should be on track at a height of 1300 ft. QFE. The pilot will then:

   (a) Stop and zero the watch.
   (b) Add power to fly level at normal base leg speed.
   (c) Start a Rate 1 turn to the right.

   The aim is to roll out of the turn and head towards the airfield on a QDM of 270°.

5. Progress of the turn can be checked by requesting a bearing at the half-way point, i.e. after 30 sec., by which time the aircraft should be midway between the outbound and inbound tracks. Outbound track was 284° = 14° more than inbound. Therefore, half way through the turn QDM will be:

$$270 + 7 = 277°.$$

If the QDM received is, for example, 280°, reduce the rate of turn slightly. If it is less than 277° the approach will have to be adjusted after flying through the extended runway centreline since instrument turns must not exceed Rate 1.

Descent to Decision Height

Before the flight the following important factors were noted while studying the approach chart:

   (a) Decision height: 820 ft.
   (b) Point at which DH will be reached: 2½ n.m. from homer.
   (c) Rate of descent: 180 ft/min.
   (d) Approach groundspeed: 80 kt.
   (e) Distance, turn to DH point: 3½ n.m.
   (f) Time, turn to DH point: 2 min. 38 sec.

Heights to achieve after 1 and 2 mins. and the final 38 seconds were previously noted on the chart as 1120 ft, 940 ft and 820 ft (Decision Height) respectively.

6. After completion of the final turn the pilot will:

   (i) Start the watch.
   (ii) Check the altimeter setting.

    (iii) Check the aircraft is trimmed at the correct speed and in the approach configuration.

    (iv) Adjust power to achieve a 180 ft/min. rate of descent.

7. Throughout the approach bearings will be requested, initially at 15–20 second intervals. If the QDMs are decreasing turn left. If the QDMs are increasing turn right.

8. At the end of 1 minute the aircraft should have descended to 1120 ft and, if not, rate of descent should be adjusted accordingly. Avoid over-correcting; headings and rates of descent should be adjusted by small amounts unless there has been a major departure from the procedure when, in extreme cases, it may be necessary to execute missed approach action.

At the end of 2 minutes the altimeter should read 940 ft and by now the aircraft should be accurately established on QDM 270° at the correct airspeed, e.g:

Groundspeed required	80 kt.
Reported wind	275°/10 kt.
Required airspeed	90 kt. (to allow for 10 kt headwind).

Approaching Decision Height

9. It should be remembered that should it be decided to initiate missed approach action height will be lost during the transition from descent to climb. While this is likely to be small in the case of most light aircraft, particularly when the rate of descent is less than 200 ft/min., the pilot must be ready to apply power early enough to prevent violating decision height.

10. Assuming there is a cloudbase of 900 ft and a RVR of 2000 m on this occasion, shortly before the end of 2 min. 38 sec. the ground will come into view. Provided visual contact with the ground is well established the approach may safely continue. However, the aircraft is still some 2½ n.m. from the homer and visibility is such that the airfield will not be in view so requests for bearings must continue.

Note. 1 on the chart says that final track is offset 3° from runway centreline (to compensate for the location of the homer) and in the final stages of the approach it will be necessary to turn right through a few degrees to regain the extended runway centreline. If, for any reason, visual contact has not been established at decision height power must be added immediately to prevent further descent.

Missed Approach/Visual Manoeuvring

The problem with a relatively high decision height such as the 820 ft required in this exercise is that it entails terminating the approach several miles from the airfield. Consequently, even if soon after reaching decision height the ground is seen, by then the aircraft could be too high to make a landing.

When, soon after decision height, the ground is seen and visibility is at least 1 n.m. a visual circuit and approach may be possible provided there is no risk of entering cloud while manoeuvring towards the runway. Loss of visual contact while near the ground has been the cause of many accidents in the past and pilots should harbour no illusions about the risks involved in trying to make a circling approach in weather that is beyond their capabilities. Minimum conditions for **Circling** are published for most airfields. In the case of Bristol Airport the limits quoted for Cat. A aircraft are a Minimum Descent Height of 600 ft (QFE) and a minimum in-flight visibility of 1900 m. When conditions are below limits missed approach action will have to be taken.

The Missed Approach

Imagine the aircraft has descended to the 820 ft decision height and visual contact has not been established. Immediately take missed approach action as follows:

1. Add power and hold the present height.
2. Maintain the present heading, advise 'Bristol Homer' of your intentions and continue obtaining QDMs to overfly the facility.
3. Note that the missed approach procedure starts from overhead the homer (see the elevation section of the chart). Obviously if the climb to 2500 ft QNH is started too soon there may be insufficient manoeuvring room for the turn back towards the homer.
4. When 'no bearing' is reported by 'Bristol Homer' continue steering the approach heading and start a climb to 2500 ft QNH (1900 ft QFE). Then level out, turn RIGHT towards the homer and climb to 3000 ft QNH (2400 ft QFE).
5. Obtain bearings to fly overhead the homer, then either fly another procedure or divert.

The QGH Procedure

The Royal Air Force and a few civil airfields operate VDF equipment as a **Ground-interpreted** aid. The procedures to be flown are much the same as already described but method of execution is totally different in so far as the pilot is required to comply with instructions passed over the RTF.

At intervals the QGH controller will call for a transmission (e.g. 'Golf Charlie Delta transmit'). On the basis of bearings shown on the VDF indicator instructions will be passed to the pilot such as 'Golf Charlie Delta steer two four zero', 'Golf Charlie Delta descend to xxx feet', etc.

Such a procedure places added responsibility on the controller but for the pilot it is simpler to fly than the VDF procedure previously described. From the cockpit the procedure is very similar to a surveillance radar approach (Chapter 8).

Conclusions

Although VDF is confined to providing bearing information it is unaffected by rain and other scatter which can lower the performance of some forms of radar. However radar, even in its simpler forms, does indicate distances as well as bearing information.

With practice VDF procedures can become simple to fly and while the greater accuracy of some other aids allows an approach to be flown to lower limits VDF remains a valuable aid.

Chapter 5
VHF Omni-directional Range (VOR)

A description of VOR and DME equipment, together with their principles of operation, is given in Chapter 11. This chapter explains its use in the air.

Station Selection and Identification

When selecting VOR stations during flight planning the following considerations should be borne in mind:

1. Terrain effect may add considerably to the errors inherent in VOR equipment (usually ±2°), but generally bearings received by VOR are accurate to within ±3°. At a distance of 60 n.m. from the facility this could mean a position line uncertainty of ±3 n.m. Although accuracy improves as the aircraft nears the VOR, the limitations of the aid should be fully realized and due allowance made for high ground which may exist on either side of the VOR radial.

2. Being a VHF aid it is subject to the usual 'line of sight' limitations, consequently pilots should not expect to receive stations at long range while flying at relatively low altitudes, particularly when there is high ground between the transmitter and the aircraft.

VOR stations are shown on Radio Navigation charts as a small compass rose with a magnetic north indicator. Nearby is a designator in the form of a small panel which gives the name in full, its three letter identification signal (transmitted in morse at 10 second intervals) and its frequency (Fig. 29).

When the station is co-related with a DME its channel number will be shown but this need not concern the pilot because VOR/DME frequencies are paired and selection of a VOR will automatically tune the DME when one is installed at the station. Most panels include the latitude and longitude of the facility. VOR stations located outside the airways system are shown along with the same information but without the surrounding frame.

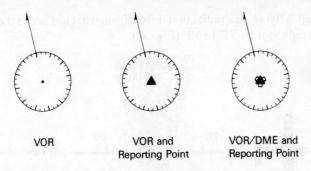

| VOR | VOR and Reporting Point | VOR/DME and Reporting Point |

Fig. 29   VOR station symbols used on AERAD charts. Magnetic Variation, east or west, is denoted by the half-arrow (left or right) on the Magnetic North Indicator.

Setting up the Nav Receiver

To ensure that the correct VOR station has been selected it is essential to check its identification signal. The volume control should be adjusted and the morse letters identified before turning down the volume again. On no account rely upon whatever VOR frequency is indicated on the NAV receiver. This part of the equipment has been known to malfunction. Also the station may not be transmitting and lack of an IDENT signal will confirm this.

After the IDENT signal has been recognized the OBS should be adjusted to ensure that signal strength is sufficient to operate the deviation needle. A sluggish needle accompanied by intermittent display of the 'NO SIGNAL' flag usually indicates that the aircraft is out of range of the VOR station.

Use of OBS, TO/FROM, NO SIGNAL and Deflection Indications

It should be remembered that full scale deflection of the deviation needle, left or right, represents approximately 10° and that is only one main division on the bearing scale which moves when the Omni-bearing Selector (OBS) is adjusted. Until the equipment has been used several times most pilots tend to adjust the OBS too coarsely and in consequence spend more time than is necessary in finding a QDM to the station.

The TO/FROM and NO SIGNAL indicators are inter-connected and during the transition from TO to FROM (or FROM to TO) the NO SIGNAL flag will appear. It will also appear at any time when the aircraft is flying on a radial that differs from what has been set on the VOR indicator by 75° to 80° (Fig. 30).

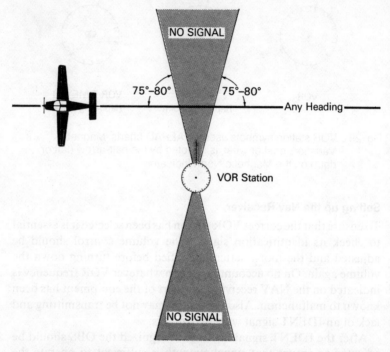

Fig. 30 The 'NO SIGNAL' flag will appear whenever the aircraft is on a radial that differs from VOR setting by more than 75° to 80°.

The TO/FROM indicator will change when the aircraft overflies the VOR station and at the same time the deviation needle usually moves rapidly across its scale. The needle may be regarded as a magnetic track, the centre of the scale representing the aircraft's position. So if while tracking towards or away from a VOR station the needle departs from centre its commands should be interpreted as:

Needle left: 'FLY LEFT'
Needle right: 'FLY RIGHT'

It should be remembered that the deviation needle will only provide corrective information when the OBS has been set so that TO is indicated while flying towards the station and FROM is showing when flying away. Non-corrective indications would occur when the bearing scale has been set on a reciprocal, e.g. 270° while flying 090° TO the station.

Determining a QDM or a Radial

The QDM to a VOR (or QDR from the station) may rapidly be found in this manner:

1. Select the correct VOR frequency on the NAV receiver, turn up the volume control, and check the ident. and NO SIGNAL flag.
2. Rotate the OBS until the deviation needle centralizes and the instrument reads TO.
3. Read QDM off the main scale (or QDR from the reciprocal scale).

Whereas QDMs are always TO the VOR station Radials are FROM (i.e. QDRs). Radials are found in the manner just described but the OBS must be set with the deviation needle centred and the instrument reading FROM.

Intercepting a given Radial (Fig. 31)

When a VOR must be approached on specific QDM a mental picture should be formed of the relationship of the aircraft to the facility and a heading flown to meet the QDM at sufficient distance from the station to allow for adjustment during the run-in.

For this example imagine that the aircraft is somewhere north of the VOR, which must be approached on a QDM of 090°.

1. Select the station frequency, identify the VOR, and determine the bearing to it, using the procedure already explained.
2. Assuming the Omni-Bearing Indicator reads 170° TO, the aircraft is slightly west of north in relation to the facility. Turn on to 200° to reach a position west of the VOR.
3. While flying on 200° set the OBS scale to read 090° (the required QDM). The deviation needle will now give a full RIGHT deflection and the NO SIGNAL flag will probably appear.
4. Continue flying to intercept 090°. When the aircraft is within 10° of this heading the deviation needle will begin to move from full RIGHT towards the central position. If the movement is rapid the aircraft is near the facility and vice versa. Lead must be allowed accordingly for the turn onto 090°. If in this case 10° lead is estimated, wait until the deviation needle is four dots RIGHT of centre then begin a rate 1 turn LEFT onto 090°.
5. When settled on 090° check that the deviation needle is in the centre and the instrument is reading TO. Make heading adjustments on the DI to compensate for drift so that the needle remains in the centre until the VOR is overflown.

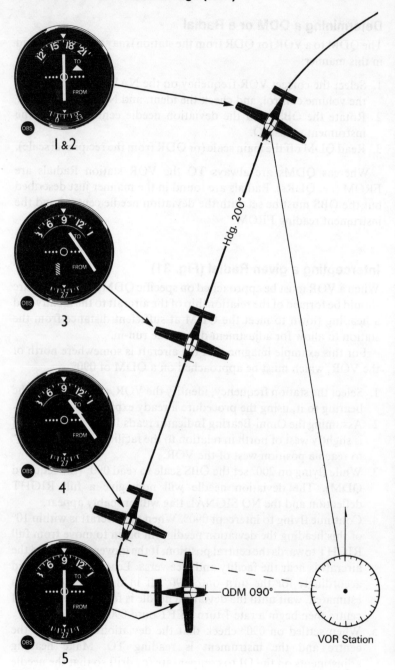

Fig. 31   Joining a QDM to the VOR station (numbers relate to the text).

Use of Radials as Position Lines

In the absence of DME progress along track may be monitored by
using a VOR suitably located to one side. When a single VOR is fitted
in the aircraft it will first be necessary to find the heading for
maintaining the required QDM to the station, allowing for drift when
this is present. Frequency can then be changed to a VOR previously
selected for the purpose of providing bearings which cross track at
positions selected at the flight planning stage.

When two VORs are installed the task is obviously simpler but
VOR position lines may also be of value while tracking towards an
NDB or in the absence of any tracking aid.

A VOR station, suitably positioned to one side of track, will enable
a pilot to avoid or find the boundary of a control zone or airway.
Proximity to the station can be assessed by timing the rate of bearing
change as described on pages 79–81.

Obtaining a Fix

A single VOR set can be used to provide a fix in the air but the task is
made simpler when bearings have been drawn, measured and noted
on the flight plan before departure.

The aircraft may be on a track not related to a VOR or other radio
facility but when it is essential to pass over a reporting or other point
this can be found by monitoring progress between the two bearings.
This will entail repeatedly changing frequency between the two
stations and adjusting the OBS to find the radials. Alternative and
easier methods of obtaining a radio fix are:

1. Using a VOR/DME bearing-and-distance when DME is available
   on the ground and in the air.
2. Using a second VOR or ADF when either is installed in the
   aircraft and suitable ground stations exist.

The accuracy of any radio fix depends upon the aircraft's
proximity to the VORs/NDBs and whether or not the two stations
selected can provide a 'cut' at a satisfactory angle. This should not be
less than 40°. Radio is an accurate measurer of distance but bearings
are affected by the 'one-in-sixty' rule and although few light aircraft
have two DMEs the most accurate radio fix would be DME/DME.

Tracking and Drift

1. Select frequency and identify the VOR as before.

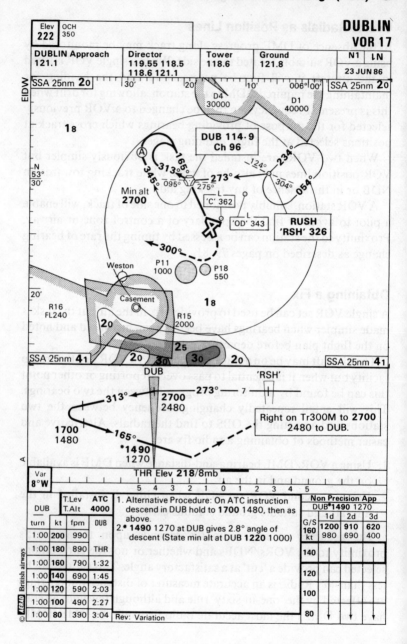

DUBLIN
VOR 17

Elev 222	OCH 350				
DUBLIN Approach 121.1	**Director 119.55 118.5 118.6 121.1**	**Tower 118.6**	**Ground 121.8**	N1	LN
				23 JUN 86	

2. Find the QDM to the facility by adjusting the OBS until the deviation needle centralizes and the instrument reads TO.
3. Turn the aircraft on to the QDM shown on the Omni-Bearing Indicator. The deviation needle will now indicate in the corrective sense.
4. Maintain heading on the DI, and if the deviation needle moves RIGHT, alter heading right to regain the QDM and centralize the needle. Each dot displacement and the edge of the circle is equivalent to $2\frac{1}{2}°$ when three dots are marked (some presentations have four when each dot and the edge of the circle represent 2°). Care must be taken not to fly with the deviation needle fully left or right, since it may be indicating a departure from QDM of more than 4 dots on the scale (10°). When the aircraft has been allowed to drift substantially off QDM the OBS should be re-set to bring the deviation needle into the scale again.
5. When the aircraft has settled on QDM with the VOR needle in the centre, compare the reading of the DI with the QDM shown on the OBS scale. The difference between the two readings represents the drift present on that heading.
6. Continue flying with the deviation needle in the centre until it swings from side to side and then settles with the instrument reading FROM. The aircraft has now flown over the VOR.

The Holding Pattern

The hold was described on page 65. In itself the racetrack pattern is simple to fly but, as previously explained, strong winds will distort its shape unless the corrective measures described are taken.

Holding patterns may be based upon a ground station (VOR, VOR/DME or NDB) or a reporting point defined on the chart as a VOR/DME bearing-and-distance. Having set the OBS to the inbound track (M), found the drift and noted the heading required to maintain the deviation needle in the centre the pattern is flown, applying the usual 'triple-drift' correction outbound (p. 67). Progress during the next turn inbound is assessed by the deviation needle.

The VOR Let-down and Approach

Golf Alpha Bravo Charlie Delta is heading for Dublin and has been advised that the ILS facility (Chapter 7) is undergoing maintenance.

An alternative aid must therefore be used for the let-down through cloud and subsequent approach. Study the DUBLIN VOR 17 approach chart on page 96 and note:

1. Airfield elevation 222 ft.
2. OCH 350 ft. Decision height would be as follows:

350 ft + 50 ft (for I/R pilots)	= 400 ft.
+ 200 ft for current IMC pilot	= 600 ft.

3. The radio frequencies for approach, tower, etc.
4. Date of chart which must be the latest published.
5. Sector safe altitudes shown in each corner of the plan section of the chart.
6. Prohibited areas D1, D4, P11, P18, R15 and R16.
7. Location of the hold based on the RUSH NDB and the hold based on the DUBLIN VOR.
8. The outbound track (M) of 313°.
9. The inbound track (M) of 165°.
10. The missed approach pattern printed in broken lines.

The elevation section shows the following information:

11. The aircraft must start the procedure by flying 273° TO the VOR from overhead the RUSH beacon at an altitude of 2700 ft (2480 ft QFE).
12. During the outbound leg and final turn a descent is made through 1000 ft. The table on the left shows the aircraft should fly outbound for 1 minute from overhead the VOR before starting a descending turn to the RIGHT onto 165° which is the extended runway centreline. This is a heading change through 212° which at Rate 1 (3°/sec.) will take 1 min. 11 sec. With the 1 minute outbound leg this means a 2 min. 11 sec. descent through 1000 ft and that will entail a rate of descent of slightly less than 500 ft/min. (actually 458 ft/min.).

    At the end of the turn the aircraft should be at 1700 ft QNH (1480 ft QFE).
13. The scale shows 4 n.m. from the turn to the VOR and another 4 n.m. from the VOR to the threshold.
14. Assuming an approach groundspeed of 80 kt, rate of descent should be 390 ft/min. and from DUB VOR to the threshold will take 3 min. 04 sec.
15. Note the missed approach procedure, which starts approximately 2 n.m. from touchdown (the approximate point where decision height will be reached), entails turning right to maintain a Tr.(M)

of 300° while climbing to 2700 ft QNH (2480 ft QFE) prior to flying over the DUBLIN VOR again.

Descent and Approach to Decision Height

The aircraft is approaching the Irish coast, homing on the RUSH beacon. When the 'over-the-beacon' indication is given by the radio compass (p. 113) a call is made to Dublin Approach, reporting overhead RUSH and requesting a VOR approach. Dublin will reply with:

> Airfield information
> Airfield weather
> Runway in use
> QNH and QFE

QNH and QFE must be read back and noted down. The VOR will be selected to the DUB frequency, the IDENT. checked and its OBS set to read 273° TO. The VOR may now be used to home overhead the station, aiming to arrive at the altitude given by ATC. The usual airfield approach checks should be completed while flying towards the VOR.

On this occasion there is no delay and there will be no need to use the hold based on DUB VOR, the aircraft having been released into the procedure:

1. Start the watch.
2. Set the OBS to 313° and fly the radial from the VOR. At first the needle may indicate maximum deviation left or right but after 30 sec. or so, when the aircraft has flown a short distance from the VOR, heading adjustments can be made to intercept the outbound QDR. The instrument should read 313° FROM.
3. Start a 450 ft/min. descent at base leg speed and after 1 minute roll into a Rate 1 descending turn to the right. Set 165° (the approach QDM) on the OBS. Complete the vital actions.
4. After 1 min. 05 sec. (i.e. the half-way point of the teardrop turn since leaving the VOR) 500 ft should have been lost and the altimeter should read 2200 ft QNH (1980 ft QFE). If not, adjust the rate of descent as required. Aim to complete the turn and roll out with the deviation needle centred on 166° TO and at a height of 1480 ft QFE.

Stop, zero and re-start the watch to time the approach.

5. Set approach flap, trim at the correct speed to provide a groundspeed of 80 kt (taking into acount the reported wind) and adjust power to produce a 390 ft/min. rate of descent. Note 2 in the chart panel advises that the State minimum height over the DUB VOR is 1000 ft QFE but to achieve a 2.8° glidepath the aircraft should be at 1270 ft QFE.

Descent to Decision Height

6. During the approach it is essential to carefully monitor the deviation needle. Remember each dot of displacement represents a departure from QDM of 2°–2½° according to dial presentation. When the needle makes the slightest departure from centre an immediate heading alteration must be made.

7. From the end of the final turn to the VOR there will be a distance of 4 n.m. to fly. When DME is fitted in the aircraft this will provide a constant progress check although it should be remembered that since it will pass over the station at 1270 ft the DME will never read less than 0.2 n.m.

    When DME is not available the stopwatch must be used. At a groundspeed of 80 kt the 4 n.m. will be covered in 3 min.

8. If the aircraft has descended to 1270 ft QFE before reaching the VOR, increase power slightly and maintain that height until the indicator changes to FROM. Should the VOR be overflown before the aircraft has descended to 1270 ft increase the rate of descent.

9. Over the VOR the deviation needle will swing and the indicator will change from TO to FROM. Report 'Golf Charlie Delta beacon inbound'. Unless the aircraft has passed directly overhead the deviation needle will be at full deflection for the first 15–30 sec. but the heading that has steered the aircraft to the VOR should be maintained. Gradually the needle will centre and the instrument will indicate 165° FROM. Make minor heading adjustments as necessary, remembering that the needle is providing correct FLY RIGHT/FLY LEFT commands since the aircraft is flying *from* the VOR and the instrument is reading FROM.

10. According to the speed table on the left there are 3 min 04 sec to run for the threshold. The aircraft must descend from 1270 ft over the VOR to the 600 ft decision height = a height loss of 670 ft at a rate of 390 ft/min. After one minute height should be 1270 – 390 = 880 ft leaving a further 280 ft to decision height.

11. At 750 ft the aircraft breaks cloud but visibility is poor and the approach lights are not in view. However, provided visual contact is firmly established at or before decision height the approach may continue but, because visibility is poor, the VOR must be used to maintain extended runway centreline while the watch indicates progress towards the threshold.
12. When the approach lights become visible the pilot should transfer from instrument to visual flight.

Missed Approach/Visual Manoeuvring

As the aircraft descends towards decision height the pilot must be prepared to apply power and climb away if visual contact has not been established. Reference to the approach chart shows that missed approach action starts at decision height. The aircraft must make a climbing turn to the right onto a magnetic track of 300°. There is no radio guidance for this leg so the pilot will have to make an estimated allowance for wind effect. In any case the leg is of short duration because, at 2700 ft QNH the aircraft may position over the DUB VOR for another approach. Alternatively, the pilot could climb to an altitude instructed by ATC and divert.

Visual Manoeuvring

The AERODROME OPERATING MINIMA page for Dublin Airport quotes a minimum descent height of 600 ft for all circling (Cat. A aircraft). A situation may have arisen during the VOR approach where, because of a slightly inaccurate VOR setting or failure to maintain the deviation needle centred during the final approach, the aircraft is displaced to one side of the runway.

Provided visual contact is firmly established without need to descend below the 600 ft MDH a circuit of the airfield, for preference keeping the runway in sight, could be flown with the permission of ATC. The VOR should remain set to the runway QDM (suitably adjusted if this was the cause of the missed approach) so that it can be used to supplement visual cues while positioning for the approach. Full use should be made of the approach lights while aligning the aircraft with the extended runway centreline.

Using DME

DME equipment is described in Chapter 11 but from the operational

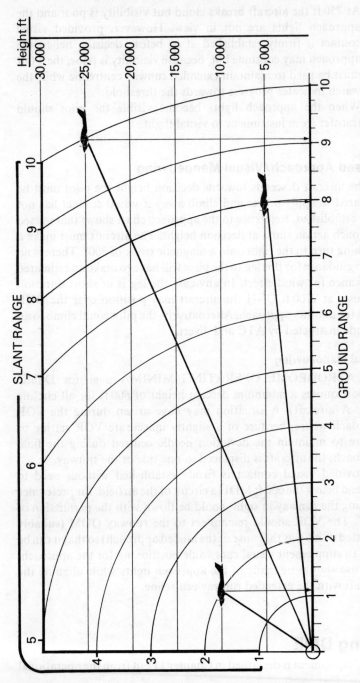

Fig. 32   Difference between Slant and Ground Range depends upon aircraft height and distance from the DME Responder.

point of view there is little the pilot must do. Frequency selection, being coupled and paired with VOR frequencies, is automatic and while many modern DMEs offer such additional features as groundspeed and time-to-the-station readouts it should be remembered that these only work while flying to or from a VOR/DME. Such information is computed within the equipment by timing rates of distance change.

Although pulse radio is a very accurate method of measuring distance it must be remembered that a DME indicates **Slant Range**. Longer distances suffer only minor difference between ground range and slant range, particularly at the altitudes normally flown by light aircraft. But at short distances, or when the aircraft is cruising at, for example, 30,000 ft, errors of this kind can be considerable. Figure 32 shows the scale of these errors. For example, an aircraft flying over a VOR/DME station at 6000 ft will never show a DME reading of less than 1 n.m. The illustration also shows that at heights of up to 5000 ft there is little difference between slant and ground range until the aircraft is within 2 n.m. of the station.

Chapter 6

Automatic Direction Finding (ADF)

The working principles of Non-Directional Beacons and ADF equipment are described in Chapter 11. Before the various air exercises are explained the following basic rules of the aid should be made clear:

1. The needle of the ADF indicator always points towards the transmitter.
2. The nose of the aircraft is represented by the instrument Lubber line.
3. If the aircraft is turned through a number of degrees, the ADF needle will turn through a corresponding number of degrees.
4. To find the QDM to a station it is necessary to add the ADF reading to the magnetic heading of the aircraft (explained on page 107 and illustrated in Fig. 33).

Station Selection and Identification

Non-Directional Beacons appear on the charts as shown below:

Note the Magnetic North Indicator for use when measuring bearings with a purpose-designed rule/protractor. Adjacent to the NDB symbol will be an information panel giving the name of the beacon, its IDENT (which, at intervals, is transmitted in morse), frequency and the lattitude and longitude of the installation.

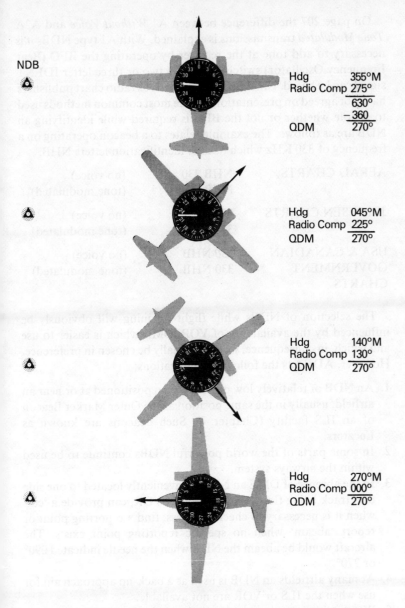

NDB

	Hdg	355°M
	Radio Comp	275°
		630°
		−360
	QDM	270°

	Hdg	045°M
	Radio Comp	225°
	QDM	270°

	Hdg	140°M
	Radio Comp	130°
	QDM	270°

	Hdg	270°M
	Radio Comp	000°
	QDM	270°

Fig. 33 Finding the QDM to the NDB by adding Magnetic Heading to the Radio Compass reading.

On page 207 the difference between A1 *Without Voice* and A2A *Tone Modulated* transmissions is explained. With A1 type NDBs it is necessary to add tone at the receiver by operating the BFO (Beat Frequency Oscillator) switch before the two or three letter IDENT signal can be heard. Unfortunately the various radio chart publishers have not agreed on presentation but the most common methods used to denote whether or not the BFO is required while identifying an NDB are as follows. The example relates to a beacon operating on a frequency of 330 KHz which has the identification letters NHB:

AERAD CHARTS	NHB 330	(no voice)
	NHB '330'	(tone modulated)
JEPPESEN CHARTS	330 *NHB*	(no voice)
	330 NHB	(tone modulated)
USA & CANADIAN GOVERNMENT CHARTS	*330* NHB	(no voice)
	330 NHB	(tone modulated)

The selection of NDBs while flight planning will obviously be influenced by the availability of VOR/DME which is easier to use and which, in consequence, would normally be chosen in preference. However, ADF has the following applications:

1. An NDB of relatively low power is often positioned at or near an airfield, usually in the same position as the Outer Marker Beacon of an ILS facility (Chapter 7). Such beacons are known as **Locators.**
2. In some parts of the world powerful NDBs continue to be used within the airways system.
3. In the absence of DME an NDB, conveniently located to one side of a track being flown with the aid of VOR, can provide a 'cut' when it is necessary to check progress, find a reporting point or report 'abeam' when no specific reporting point exists. The aircraft would be abeam the NDB when the needle indicated 090° or 270°.
4. At many airfields an NDB is used as a back-up approach aid for use when the ILS or VOR are not available.
5. When it is convenient to do so, domestic broadcasting stations may be used for navigational purposes. There are also the marine beacons located around the coast but these only transmit for brief periods at intervals of 6 minutes and they are not ideal for aeronautical purposes.

Pre-flight Checks and Identifying the NDB

The beacons to be used should be noted on the flight plan along with their frequencies and any relevant bearing information that may be required for obtaining a fix, etc. Operation in the aircraft may vary slightly according to the make and design of the equipment but typically it is simply a matter of:

1. Before flight finding an NDB on the chart that is within 50 n.m. of the airfield and selecting the required frequency.
2. Checking if the NDB requires the use of the BFO switch to add a tone to the transmission. If not:
3. Selecting ANT (antenna) on the function switch then turning up the volume control and checking the IDENT which may take the form of two or three letters. The switch is then returned to the ADF position (some equipment is marked AUTO).
4. Lining up the aircraft on the QDM to the NDB when the ADF indicator should read zero.
5. As a further check on equipment serviceability the function switch should be turned to ANT when the needle will settle on 090°. When it is returned to the ADF position the needle should swing positively to the NDB.

Relationship between ADF Indicator and Magnetic Headings

When an ADF Indicator points towards the NDB to which it is tuned it is providing a **Relative Bearing,** i.e. the angle between the aircraft's fore and aft axis and the QDM to the beacon. Figure 33 shows that, to obtain the QDM to the beacon, it is necessary to add the magnetic heading being flown to the ADF indicator reading. When the total exceeds 360° the bearing is ascertained by subtracting 360.

To avoid the need for mental arithmetic, particularly at times of high workload, most modern ADF indicators incorporate an adjustable bearing scale which may be aligned with aircraft heading so that ADF needle indications represent QDMs to the beacon. In Fig. 34 both aircraft are flying on a magnetic heading of 030°. The upper aircraft has an ADF indicator with a fixed dial which is reading 270° and to obtain the QDM to the beacon it is necessary to add Hdg(M) to relative bearing:

$$30 + 270 = 300°.$$

The lower aircraft has an ADF indicator fitted with an adjustable dial. This has been set by the pilot to agree with magnetic heading and

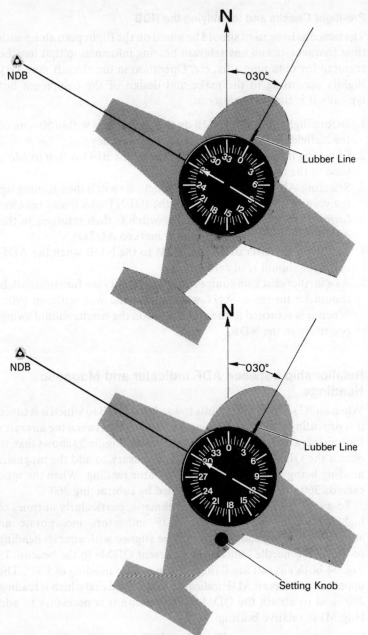

Fig. 34   Advantages of an ADF Indicator fitted with an adjustable dial
          which may be aligned with Magnetic Heading to provide a
          QDM without need of addition as in Fig. 33.

the ADF now reads 300° which is the QDM to the beacon. A further refinement found on larger aircraft is the **Radio Magnetic Indicator (RMI)** which incorporates a moving scale operated by a gyro-magnetic compass. Such an instrument will indicate QDMs to the beacon without need of adjusting the scale. In still more developed form RMIs with two needles indicating bearings simultaneously from two NDBs (or an NDB and a VOR) have the advantage of providing an instant navigational fix. The RMI is rarely fitted in light single-engine aircraft.

Use of Relative Bearings in en route Navigation

It is often important to establish progress along track, sometimes when no suitable DME or VOR facilities are available. In Fig. 35 the aircraft is flying from over the sea towards a VOR on a QDM of 260° and the pilot wishes to report 'crossing the coast' to ATC.

On this occasion the pilot is above cloud and unable to see the ground but there is an NDB situated north of track and a QDM of

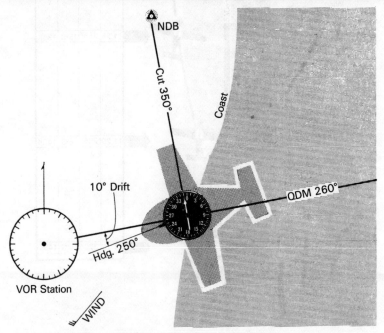

Fig. 35   Using an NDB to provide a Cut while flying towards another radio facility. The ADF Indicator has been adjusted to the 250° heading being flown to compensate for drift.

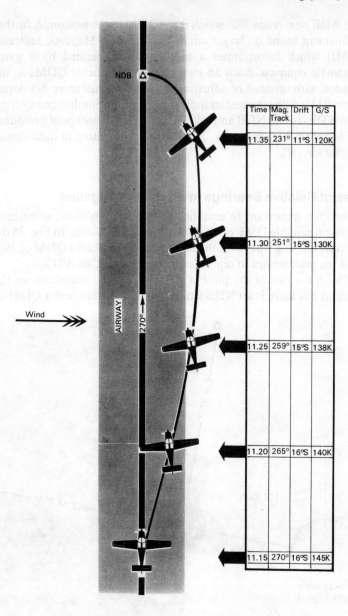

Time	Mag. Track	Drift	G/S
11.35	231°	11°S	120K
11.30	251°	15°S	130K
11.25	259°	15°S	138K
11.20	265°	16°S	140K
11.15	270°	16°S	145K

Fig. 36   TMG (Track Made Good) while maintaining the ADF Indicator on zero in the presence of a 40 kt crosswind.

350° crosses the 260° magnetic track to the VOR to provide a fix directly over the coast. There is a 10° drift correction so the pilot is having to steer a Hdg(M) of 350°. This has been set on the ADF Indicator so that when the needle reads 350° the aircraft is over the coast.

Homing to an NDB and the Effects of Drift

Although it may be used on other occasions, the following procedure is often adopted when flying along an airway. After selecting the relevant station on the radio navigation chart, and after selecting the correct frequency and confirming the beacon identification, turn the aircraft until the ADF needle indicates zero. Check the heading of the aircraft on the DI to confirm that the ADF is not giving a totally incorrect indication, as it would, for example, if it were tuned to the wrong NDB. The aircraft will eventually arrive over the station.

The presence of drift entails some form of correction because, although the aircraft will ultimately arrive over the station, its path will curve increasingly towards the transmitter. Figure 36 shows what would happen to an aircraft flying along an airway in the presence of a 40 kt crosswind component, assuming the pilot were to maintain the ADF needle at zero throughout. Although the NDB is eventually overflown, at one stage the airway is departed and the vital reporting point is by-passed. This is unacceptable and to remain within an airway the correct QDM must be maintained.

Assessment of, and compensation for, drift is made by using the following procedure in which the step-by-step numbering relates to aircraft nos. 1 to 5 in Fig. 37.

1. For this exercise the required QDM is 270° and the aircraft is positioned on it steering 270° on the DI. The ADF scale has been aligned with the DI so its needle will initially indicate 270° because it is pointing to the NDB.
2. Soon after attaining the QDM a wind from the left causes drift to the right and this is confirmed by the ADF which is now reading 260°.
3. Corrections must now be applied to compensate for drift and to regain the required QDM.
   Such corrections are a matter of trial and error but a heading alteration of 25° left (i.e. 2½ times drift) would be appropriate in this case. The DI would now read 245° and this should be set on the ADF scale. During this phase of the correction the ADF needle will be reading 260°.

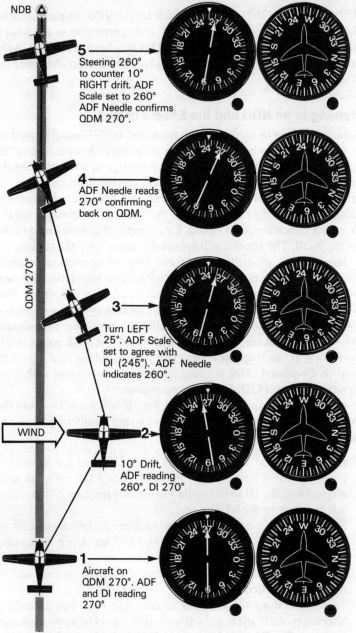

NDB

5
Steering 260°
to counter 10°
RIGHT drift. ADF
Scale set to 260°
ADF Needle confirms
QDM 270°.

4
ADF Needle reads
270° confirming
back on QDM.

QDM 270°

3
Turn LEFT
25°. ADF Scale
set to agree with
DI (245°). ADF Needle
indicates 260°.

WIND

2
10° Drift,
ADF reading
260°, DI 270°

1
Aircraft on
QDM 270°. ADF
and DI reading
270°

Fig. 37   Correct use of the ADF Indicator and Direction Indicator to
avoid the situation shown in Fig. 36 (numbers adjacent to the
aircraft relate to the text).

4. Hold the new heading on the DI and as the aircraft closes with the correct QDM the ADF needle will gradually increase its reading. When it indicates aircraft Hdg(M) plus the 25° correction (i.e. 245 + 25 = 270°) the required QDM has been regained.

5. The present heading (245°) would fly the aircraft through and to the left of QDM so it must be increased but not to the point where drift would occur again. The number of degrees to allow must at this stage be estimated but, in this example, after minor adjustments a heading of 260° is found to hold the aircraft on a QDM of 270° to the NDB. A heading of 260° is set on the ADF scale and the needle will then indicate 270° which is the required QDM.

Station Transit

Like any radio aid providing bearings from a fixed point ADF becomes more sensitive as the aircraft nears the beacon and the bearings converge like the spokes of a cycle wheel.

Like VOR or VDF the only position provided by ADF is when the aircraft overflies the facility. As the range between aircraft and NDB decreases so the ADF needle will become increasingly sensitive to aircraft displacement left or right of the QDM. When the aircraft passes to one side of the NDB the ADF needle will follow the transmitter through 180°. If, by very accurate flying, the aircraft actually flies overhead the NDB the needle will swing rapidly through 180°.

Although ADF Indicators do not have a TO/FROM arrow or flag the 'over-the-beacon' signal provided when the ADF needle swings through 180° is unmistakable.

Intercepting an Outbound Track

It is often necessary to fly outbound on a specified Tr(M) from the NDB. Figure 38 shows an aircraft approaching the beacon on a QDM of 270°. When the beacon is overflown the pilot could gain the 360° QDR from the NDB by turning left through 270° and flying over the NDB again on the new heading but this method would be quicker:

1. On obtaining the 'over-the-beacon' indication turn right onto 360° + 15° to allow for the radius of turn = 015°.

2. Hold 015° on the DI and set that heading on the ADF bearing scale.

6 Automatic Direction Finding (ADF)

3. Remember that the ADF needle always points to the NDB (Rule 1, page 104), therefore although the aircraft is required to fly on a QDR of 360° *away* from the beacon the ADF will only indicate QDMs. In other words, when flying away from an NDB the ADF needle will point to the tail of the aircraft. In this case when the ADF needle reads 180° the 360° outbound track has been intercepted.

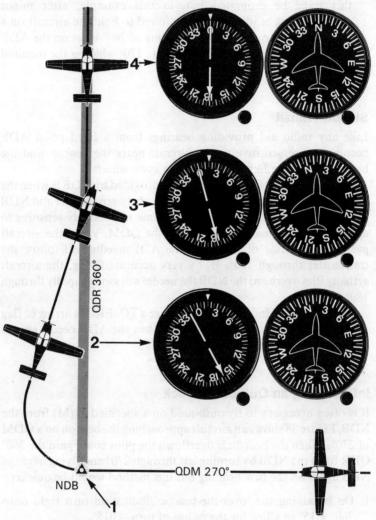

Fig. 38   Joining a QDR from the NDB after over-flying the facility (numbers relate to the text).

4. Turn the aircraft onto 360°, adjust the ADF scale to 360° and assuming there is no wind the QDR will be maintained with the ADF indicating 180°.

Correcting for Drift

It is important to develop a mental picture of the relationship between aircraft and beacon. In the example just described the NDB is directly behind the pilot and if the needle moves, say slightly to the left it is saying "the beacon is behind your left shoulder and the aircraft has drifted right". Appropriate corrections can then be made to compensate for right drift by turning left.

Full use should be made of the adjustable bearing scale on the ADF Indicator so that it provides QDMs to the NDB at all times.

Procedural and en-route Holding Patterns

Most holding patterns within the airways system are these days based on a VOR or VOR/DME but at airfields an NDB is often the source of reference. Methods of joining a hold are much the same as for VOR in so far as the patterns to be flown depend upon the direction of entry to the 'racetrack'. This is illustrated on page 66 (Fig. 20).

Techniques to be adopted while flying a teardrop procedure turn (Fig. 19), the hold (Fig. 21) and compensating for drift during a procedure turn (Fig. 22), which were described on pages 65 to 71, all apply to ADF. It must be acknowledged that the various procedures are more difficult to fly accurately on ADF than with the aid of VOR, particularly when the VOR is co-related with DME. VOR provides fixed bearings/radials which, even with a basic VOR indicator, are presented in semi-pictorial form; the deviation needle may be regarded as the QDM/QDR. Conversely, establishing the aircraft on a particular QDM/QDR with the aid of an NDB entails interpreting direction indicator readings to establish heading in conjunction with ADF readings to determine whether or not the beacon is, for example, straight ahead of the aircraft or to one side.

Like most elements of flying, instrument or visual, mastery can only be gained through practice.

The NDB Let-down and Approach

As well as providing en-route navigational aid ADF may be used for the let-down and approach. In this example the aircraft is flying

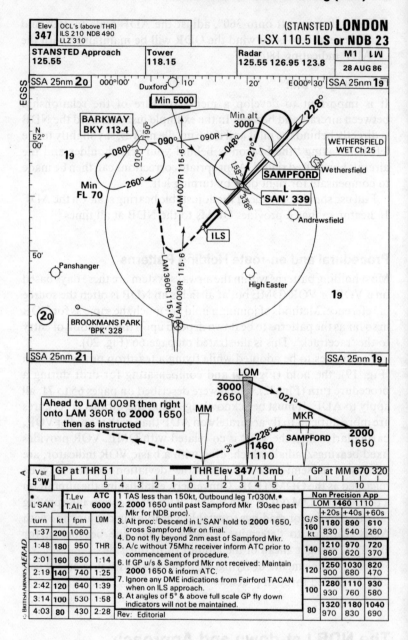

towards London Stansted Airport from the south. Study the (STANSTED) LONDON ILS or NDB 23 approach chart which appears on page 116 and note:

1. Airfield elevation which is 347 ft.
2. OCL (NDB) 490 ft. Decision height would be as follows:

    490 ft + 50 ft (for I/R pilots) = 540 ft.

    +200 ft for current IMC pilot = 740 ft.

3. The radio frequencies for approach, tower, etc.
4. Date of chart which must be the latest published.
5. Sector safe altitudes shown in each corner of the plan section of the chart.
6. Notes 1 to 5 in the information panel.
7. Position of the locator NDB (Ident. letters SAN, tone modulated) and the SAMPFORD fan marker (described on page 00).
8. The outbound track (M) of 030° for aircraft with a TAS of less than 150 kt (Note 1).
9. The inbound track (M) of 228°M and the need to remain at a height of 1650 ft until 30 seconds after passing the SAMPFORD fan marker (Note 2).
10. The missed approach pattern printed in broken lines.

The Elevation Section shows the following information:

11. The aircraft must start the procedure by arriving over the NDB at 3000 ft QNH (2650 ft QFE). Alternatively it may enter the SAN hold and descend to 2000 ft QNH after clearance from ATC to commence the approach (Note 3).
12. During the outbound leg a descent is made through 1000 ft.
13. The scale shows 6 n.m. from the turn to the NDB and a further 3.25 n.m. from the NDB to the runway threshold.
14. Assuming an approach groundspeed of 80 kt, rate of descent should be 430 ft/min. from 30 sec. past the SAMPFORD fan marker. From the NDB to the threshold will take 2 min. 28 sec.
15. Reference to the *Non Precision Approach* table on the right shows the following target heights to be attained after flying over the NDB:

after 20 seconds	970 ft QFE
after 40 seconds	830 ft QFE
after 60 seconds	690 ft QFE

However decision height for an IMC rated pilot flying this

procedure has been calculated as 740 ft and on the basis of the figures provided in the panel this will be reached 52 seconds after flying through the NDB (i.e. a descent from 1110 ft to 740 ft = 370 ft at a rate of 430 ft/min). **This must be calculated and noted, if possible prior to the flight but certainly before the approach.**

16. Note the missed approach procedure which entails climbing straight ahead to intercept the 009° radial from LAMBOURNE VOR before turning right and continuing the climb on radial 360° from that VOR until 2000 ft QNH (1650 ft QFE) and then as instructed by ATC. Since this involves the use of radials from the LAMBOURNE VOR the equipment must be set up *before* starting the procedure so that a missed approach can safely be conducted if required.

Descent and Approach to Decision Height

While approaching Stansted the pilot will call: 'Stansted Approach, Golf Alpha Bravo Charlie Delta, Piper Arrow, approaching from the south, Flight Level six five, estimating the zone boundary [a reference to the Stansted Special Rules Zone which extends from ground level to FL65] at three two [32 minutes past the hour] for NDB approach'.

Stansted will reply: 'Golf Charlie Delta is cleared to the Stansted beacon. Descend to three thousand feet, QNH xxx'. ATC will also transmit airfield information, airfield weather, runway in use, QNH and QFE

QNH and QFE must be noted down and read back.

Had there been a delay 'Charlie Delta' would have been placed in the hold, either at BARKWAY (minimum FL70) or on the Stansted NDB (minimum altitude 3000 ft QNH). On this occasion the pilot is cleared for a direct approach to the beacon. While flying towards the NDB he will:

(i)   Complete the FREDA checks.
(ii) Report leaving Flight Level 65.
(iii) Report level at 3000 ft on the QNH.

While nearing the NDB it is important to trim the aircraft at the appropriate speed listed in the left-hand table. This will depend on the aircraft type but remember that the table shows *groundspeeds* and an allowance for wind must be made. In this case there will be a 20 kt tailwind so an IAS of 120 kt would relate to a 140 kt outbound leg which, the table shows, must be flown for 2 min. 19 sec. before the start of the turn. The following sequence is probably more easily flown by leaving the ADF bearing scale set on 360° although some pilots prefer to align it with magnetic heading.

1. When the ADF indicates 'over-the-beacon' call 'Golf Charlie Delta beacon outbound' and
    (a) Turn onto 030°.
    (b) Start the watch.
    (c) Commence a 450 ft/min. rate of descent and aim to arrive at 2000 ft QNH at the end of 2 min. 19 sec.
    (d) Complete the pre-landing vital actions.
    (e) Double check the altimeter setting(s).

2. While flying outbound check for drift. If the ADF moves away from 180° (beacon behind the tail) turn in the same direction as needle displacement and hold the new heading until the needle moves back towards 180°. Then steer 030° +/− drift with the ADF indicating the same number of degrees allowance left or right of 180°.

3. After 1 min. 10 sec. the aircraft should have descended to 2500 ft. If not adjust rate of descent accordingly. The SAMPFORD fan marker may be heard as the aircraft flies through the edge of its radiation pattern. If the aircraft has descended to 2000 ft QNH before the end of the 2 min. 19 sec. outbound period, level out and prevent further loss of height.

4. After 2 min. 19 sec. level out, start a Rate 1 turn to the right and zero the stopwatch. Check progress of the turn on the ADF and aim to intercept the 228° approach QDM. If, on rolling out on a heading of 228°, the ADF needle is pointing to the right of the nose increase the heading according to the amount of displacement. If the ADF needle is to the left of the nose decrease the heading. Aim to be settled on a QDM of 228° before reaching the SAMPFORD marker.

5. Hold 2000 QNH (1650 ft QFE) and trim at the approach speed. For a light single 80 kt groundspeed would be convenient but since there is a 20 kt wind reported this will entail an IAS of 100 kt and a descent rate of 430 ft/min. (left-hand panel on the chart). **For this procedure the descent must not start until 30 seconds after flying over the SAMPFORD marker** (Note 2).

6. The SAMPFORD marker will at first be faint, gradually becoming louder with the marker light flashing as the aircraft approaches the beam centre. When the signal is being received at full strength the watch should be started.

Descent to Decision Height

Throughout the approach a careful check must be made on the ADF to ensure that the aircraft is not drifting left or right of extended runway centreline. When there is no crosswind the needle should remain on 360° provided the pilot is steering the correct runway QDM. If, for example, it is necessary to counter 10° left drift, heading in this case would be 228° + 10° = 238° and the ADF would be indicating 10° left of the nose = 350°.

The descent to decision height would continue as follows:

7. At the end of 30 seconds since flying over the SAMPFORD marker a 430 ft/min. descent must be started. The aircraft should fly over the NDB at a height of 1100 ft QFE. Thereafter the threshold will be reached after 2 min. 28 sec. assuming a groundspeed of 80 kt. In preparation for this the watch should be zeroed.

8. Reference to the *Non Precision Approach* table on the right of the chart shows the target heights to be achieved 20, 40 and 60 seconds after overflying the NDB. However decision height has been established at 740 ft and it was previously calculated that this will be reached 52 seconds after leaving the NDB (item 15 on pages 117/118).

9. If the aircraft has descended to 1100 ft QFE *before* overflying the NDB further height loss must be prevented until the 'over-the-beacon' indication is shown on the ADF. When the ADF needle swings through 180° call 'Golf Charlie Delta beacon inbound' and start the watch.
   ATC will respond with 'Golf Charlie Delta, clear to land' and give the surface wind.

10. ATC are reporting unbroken cloud at 1100 ft and 5 octas at 800 ft so the weather is near the ceiling limit for this approach. However RVR is reported as 5 km so provided the aircraft is not displaced from the extended runway centreline the transition from instrument to visual approach should not present any problems.

11. After 20 seconds the aircraft is at 1020 ft which is 50 ft above the glidepath. Rate of descent must be increased slightly. After 40 seconds the altimeter reads 800 ft which is 30 ft below the glidepath. By now the aircraft is flying in and out of the base of cloud.

12. 50 seconds after leaving the NDB the aircraft is at 750 ft. Here and there traces of cloudbase occur but the ground below is clear,

the approach lights appear and the descent may safely continue
for a visual final approach to land.

Missed Approach/Visual Manoeuvring

Had the aircraft emerged from cloud badly displaced to the left or
right of extended runway centreline, or if poor visibility and lower
than reported cloud had obscured the approach lights a missed
approach would have been necessary. It would be conducted as
follows:

1. Apply climbing power and maintain the present heading. Advise
   Stansted Tower that Golf Charlie Delta is going around.

2. The LAMBOURNE VOR, previously set for the 009° radial from
   the station, (see item 16 on page 118) will be used to indicate the
   start of the turn.

3. When the VOR needle centres start a Rate 1 turn to the right and
   reset the OBS to 360°. The instrument should continue reading
   FROM. When the needle centres continue climbing on that radial
   and level out at 2000 ft QNH. Further instructions will be passed
   by Stansted ATC.

Visual Manoeuvring

Reference to the AERODROME OPERATING MINIMA page for
Stansted in the airways manual shows that for aircraft not exceeding
5700 kg MTWA (Maximum Take-off Weight Authorized) the
minimum circling height is 600 ft. This is quoted as a decision height
but for aircraft flying at 100 kt a visibility of not less than 2000 metres
would be required and 200 metres should be added for every
additional 10 kt of circuit speed.

As 2000 metres is little more than 1 n.m., when the visibility is on or
near the limit it will not be easy to keep the runway in view while
circling to join the approach. The ADF should be used to assist in
assessing the relationship between aircraft and runway threshold
while flying downwind and while aligning with the extended runway
centreline for the approach. Naturally all circling should be
conducted at reduced speed and with part flap (i.e. low safe cruising
speed technique. This is described on pages 234/5 of *Flight Briefing
for Pilots, Volume 1*).

Conclusions

Although in most of the developed areas of the world ADF has been largely replaced by VOR/DME as an airways aid, it continues to be employed as a locator at many airfields. Such NDBs are usually of low power and they have a range of 10–20 n.m.

In less developed parts of the world the NDB remains in service. The ground station is less complex than a VOR, cheaper to install and maintain and the more powerful beacons will provide reasonably accurate bearings over distances of up to 100 n.m. under good conditions. However, during thunderstorms ADF must be used with particular care since the needle will often tend to seek the storm in preference to the NDB. Intelligent use of the direction indicator and, whenever possible, the confirmation of a VOR radial, should be used to prevent serious navigational mistakes due to erroneous ADF indications.

Chapter 7
Instrument Landing System (ILS)

ILS is a short-range precision approach aid which provides accurate guidance along the extended runway centreline and down the glidepath. To assist in intercepting the localizer (described on page 125) one or more of the following aids will be provided:

Surveillance radar (Chapters 8 and 11)
NDB locators (Chapter 6, page 106 and Chapter 11)
VOR (Chapters 5 and 11)
VDF (Chapters 4 and 11)

One of the advantages of ILS is its ability to allow relatively high landing rates at busy airports although, when heavy traffic exists, it is often necessary to **Stack** aircraft in a holding pattern. The holds may be positioned on standard arrival routes or at the destination but the racetrack pattern will usually be based on an NDB or a VOR although there are exceptions where the holding point is located on a specified bearing-and-distance from a convenient VOR/DME station. IMC rated pilots would not normally be expected to fly such a hold.

When a number of aircraft are awaiting clearance to join airfield traffic they may be stacked at 1000 ft intervals within the hold. The hold was described on page 65.

Station Selection and Identification

Full details of ILS facilities at the various airfields are listed in the AERAD Supplement and the ILS approach charts for each runway. These include ILS frequencies, glidepath angle (usually 3°), IDENT signals, category (e.g. Cat. 3 means the installation is cleared for Autoland approaches by suitably equipped aircraft: light aircraft equipment is usually Cat. 1), and hours of operation. There may also be special notices warning of possible local disturbances to the localizer or glidepath due to siting difficulties. These are usually of a minor nature.

Using a VOR installation for ILS Approaches

ILS can be received and used on VOR equipment although there will be no glidepath indications. The OBS selector does not function when the NAV receiver is set to an ILS frequency.

Without glidepath information the accuracy of ILS will obviously be reduced and the approach chart will quote a higher OCH/OCL when localizer only procedures are to be flown. The figure for OCH/OCL will be preceded by the letters LLZ signifying localizer only.

Selection and Identification of the ILS

As ILS is a short range aid the aircraft must usually be within 25 n.m. of the airfield before signals can be received. The published frequency should be set on the NAV receiver and the volume increased so that the IDENT letters can be interpreted. Selection of the localizer frequency will automatically set the correct glidepath frequency since these are paired by international agreement. However, when a Marker Receiver is fitted this will usually need to be switched on separately.

ILS installations are supported by one or more locator beacons and these too will be of low power since their purpose is to help position the aircraft onto the localizer. Some airfields also offer DME facilities which provide 'distance-to-threshold' readouts on a constant basis. All such frequencies must be noted on the flight plan prior to take-off so that the various facilities and their IDENTS can be identified while flying towards the destination.

'No Signal' Indications

Although ATC will advise of any installation malfunction at the airfield (e.g. the glidepath transmitter or a marker could have failed or the ILS may be under maintenance), should, for any reason, the aircraft receiver be unable to provide a suitable output to the ILS indicator the 'NO SIGNAL' flag will appear adjacent to the needle affected.

If ATC confirms that the ILS is functioning correctly yet both warning flags are showing the following steps should be taken:

1. Check the frequency being displayed on the NAV receiver and if it is incorrect re-set the equipment.
2. If the correct frequency is showing turn up the volume and check the IDENT in case the frequency indicator has become out of

phase with the selector knobs. The selector should be adjusted in steps above and below the indicated frequency in an effort to bring in the correct IDENT. Should this fail —

3. Try a VOR frequency to check if the receiver is operating. If not, the receiver is unserviceable

Approach to the Facility using the Locator and/or Radar Vectoring

To help position an aircraft on the ILS airfields will have one or more locator beacons. The approach chart will show the pattern to be flown and the altitude/height at which to fly overhead one or more of these NDBs. There may be a hold based on these locators although at the busier international airports holds are usually sited some distance from the airfield.

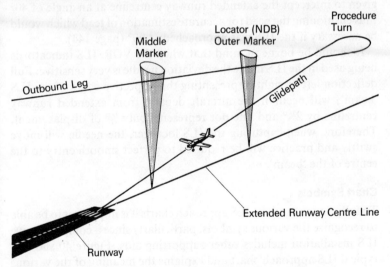

Fig. 39 Simplified ILS procedure showing the relationship of the Outbound Leg, Procedure Turn, Glidepath and Markers.

Locators are usually co-sited with the ILS outer marker beacon. They are shown on approach charts with the letters LOM (Locator and Outer Marker). Being on the extended runway centreline they are ideally positioned to guide an aircraft onto the ILS localizer, usually via a procedure which entails flying in the reverse to landing direction at above circuit height followed by a descent and a procedure turn back towards the runway. At that stage the localizer will have been captured and the remainder of the procedure is then flown with reference to the localizer and glidepath needles in conjunction with the flight instruments (Fig. 39).

Radar Vectoring

A very convenient and usually faster method of aligning the aircraft with the ILS is known as **Radar Vectoring**. As the name implies aircraft cleared for an approach are given a series of headings to steer by the airfield radar controller. Usually surveillance radar is operated on the 'Radar' and/or 'Approach' frequency. Radar vectoring area charts are published for the purpose and these are described in Chapter 8.

Generally the controller will aim to position the aircraft on a base leg that is somewhat further downwind than usual. To assist the pilot in gradually capturing the ILS localizer a heading change will be given to intercept the extended runway centreline at an angle of 40° thus cushioning the need for accurate estimation of lead which would be necessary if the ILS was approached at 90° (page 144).

It should be borne in mind that when the VOR/ILS indicator is being used in the ILS mode the deviation needle is very sensitive. Full deflection left or right (representing the respective edges of the ILS 'beam') will occur if the aircraft departs from extended runway centreline by $2\frac{1}{2}°$ and one dot represents only $\frac{1}{2}°$ of displacement. Therefore, when capturing the ILS localizer, the needle will move swiftly and practice will be required to perfect smooth entry to the centre of the 'beam'.

Chart Symbols

To fully understand the ILS approach charts it is important to be able to recognize the various symbols, particularly since a comprehensive ILS installation includes other supporting aids. Figure 40 shows a typical ILS approach chart and explains the meaning of the various symbols. Some of these may not appear on all charts.

Orientation and Identification of Locator, Localizer, Glidepath and Markers

As previously mentioned, the entire airfield installation (described on page 217 of Chapter 11) embraces two separate transmitters for guidance towards the runway (localizer and glidepath), one or more locators (low powered NDBs) and usually two markers (Outer and Middle). There may also be a co-related DME.

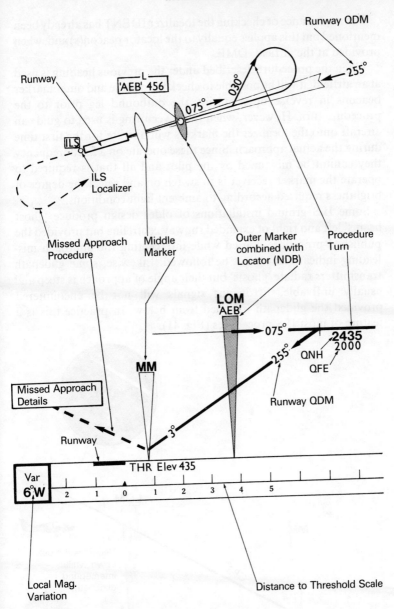

Fig. 40   Simplified ILS Approach Chart, showing the various symbols used in the Plan and Elevation sections.

The importance of checking the localizer IDENT has already been mentioned but this applies equally to the locator beacon(s) and, when provided at the airfield, DME.

When the procedure described under the previous heading is used at an airfield, it will be possible to check the middle and outer marker beacons in reverse order during the outbound leg prior to the procedure turn. However, when radar vectoring is used to guide an aircraft onto the localizer the markers will operate for the first time during the actual approach. Since these operate on a fixed frequency they cannot be mis-tuned by the pilot and all that is required to operate the marker receiver is to switch on and select the degree of brightness required according to ambient light conditions.

Some ILS ground installations of older design produce 'ghost beams' left and right of extended runway centreline but provided the published procedure is used while intercepting the approach misleading indications cannot be followed. Likewise, some glidepath transmitters radiate 'ghosts' but their angle of approach is steep and usually unflyable. Erroneous signals will not be encountered provided the glidepath is joined from below. In practice this is a feature of most ILS procedures (Fig. 41).

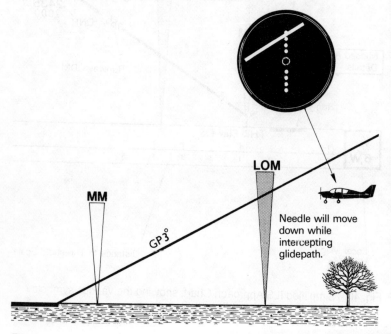

Fig. 41   Joining the Glidepath from below to avoid 'Ghost' indications.

The Holding Pattern

When an ILS procedure includes a hold its axis will often be aligned with the runway QDM. There are, however, exceptions when for local reasons the inbound/outbound legs of the hold do not comply with the QDR/QDM of the runway. Alternatively the hold may be based on a VOR or an NDB located some distance from the airfield. Ground facilities and their location relative to the airfield vary according to traffic requirements, the proximity of other airfields and/or controlled airspace and local features such as high ground, built up areas, etc.

Students training for the IMC Rating can learn a lot about ILS and other approach procedures by studying a variety of charts for different airfields.

The ILS Approach

The example used for this air exercise is based on the ILS for Runway 24 at Manchester International Airport. Study the MANCHESTER INTL ILS or LLZ/DME [localizer only in conjunction with DME] chart reproduced on page 128 and note:

1. Airfield elevation which is 256 ft.
2. OCL (Cat. 1 ILS equipment) 170 ft. Decision height:
   170 ft + 50 ft (for I/R pilots)   = 220 ft.
   + 200 ft for current IMC pilot = 420 ft.
3. The radio frequencies for approach, tower, etc.
4. Date of chart which must be the latest published.
5. Sector safe altitudes shown in each corner of the plan section of the chart.
6. Prohibited/restricted areas D304 and D314.
7. Location of:
   (a) The BARTON hold (min FL 50) based on the BTN VOR/DME.
   (b) The DAYNE hold (min FL50) located on a bearing-and-distance from BARTON VOR.
   (c) The **Alternative Hold** shown in dotted lines with a letter A in a circle. This is based on the CONGLETON NDB.
   (d) The hold upwind of the runway shown in broken lines (minimum altitude 3000 ft) which is flown on the 'MCR' locator following a missed approach.
   (e) The procedure hold (minimum altitude 3000 ft) based on the 'ME' locator.

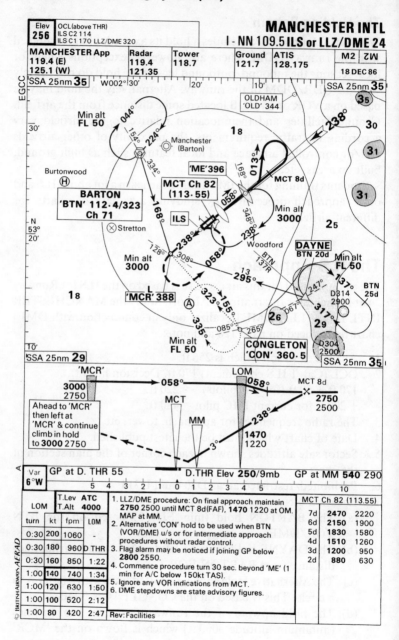

MANCHESTER INTL
I - NN 109.5 ILS or LLZ/DME 24

Elev 256	OCL(above THR) ILS C2 114 ILS C1 170 LLZ/DME 320

MANCHESTER App 119.4 (E) 125.1 (W)	Radar 119.4 121.35	Tower 118.7	Ground 121.7	ATIS 128.175	M2 ZW 18 DEC 86

EGCC   SSA 25nm 35   W002°30'   20'   10'   SSA 25nm 35

OLDHAM 'OLD' 344

Min alt FL 50   044°   154°   224°   334°   Manchester (Barton)   238°   35   30   31   31

'ME' 396   168°   013°   MCT 8d

Burtonwood (H)   MCT Ch 82 (113·55)   058°   348°   Min alt 3000

BARTON 'BTN' 112·4/323 Ch 71   ILS   238°   238°   25

⊗ Stretton   238°   058°   Woodford   DAYNE BTN 20d   Min alt FL 50

N 53° 20'   128°   308°   BTN 137R   137°   247°   BTN 25d

Min alt 3000   295°   13   D314 2900

1 8   'MCR' 388   (A)   323°   155°   317°   29

335°   085°   265°   2 6   D304 2500

10'   Min alt FL 50   CONGLETON 'CON' 360·5   SSA 25nm 35

SSA 25nm 29

'MCR'   LOM   MCT 8d
3000 2750   —058°—   058°   × 2750 2500

Ahead to 'MCR' then left at 'MCR' & continue climb in hold to 3000 2750   MCT   238°
MM   3°   1470 1220

| Var 6°W | GP at D. THR 55 | D.THR Elev 250/9mb | GP at MM 540 290 |

5   4   3   2   1   0   1   2   3   4   5   10

LOM	T.Lev ATC T.Alt 4000			1. LLZ/DME procedure: On final approach maintain 2750 2500 until MCT 8d(FAF), 1470 1220 at OM. MAP at MM.	MCT Ch 82 (113.55)
turn	kt	fpm	LOM	2. Alternative 'CON' hold to be used when BTN (VOR/DME) u/s or for intermediate approach procedures without radar control.	7d 2470 2220
0:30	200	1060	-		6d 2150 1900
0:30	180	960	D THR	3. Flag alarm may be noticed if joining GP below 2800 2550.	5d 1830 1580
0:30	160	850	1:22	4. Commence procedure turn 30 sec. beyond 'ME' (1 min for A/C below 150kt TAS).	4d 1510 1260
1:00	140	740	1:34	5. Ignore any VOR indications from MCT.	3d 1200 950
1:00	120	630	1:50	6. DME stepdowns are state advisory figures.	2d 880 630
1:00	100	520	2:12		
1:00	80	420	2:47	Rev: Facilities	

© BRITISH AIRWAYS AERAD

130

Note there is a DME (IDENT letters MCT) near the runway threshold. In aircraft with two NAV receivers the ILS could be selected on one of them (109.5 MHz) and the VOR frequency shown thus, (113.55), would bring in Channel 82 for the DME. During an ILS approach DME can provide valuable 'distance-to-threshold' information but there is a warning (Note 5 in the information panel) to ignore any VOR indications since there is no VOR transmitter sited with the DME.

8.   The outbound track (M) of 058°.

9.   The inbound track (M) of 238°.

10. The missed approach pattern printed in broken lines.

The Elevation Section shows the following information:

11. The aircraft must start the procedure by positioning over the 'MCR' locator at 3000 ft QNH (2750 ft QFE) and maintain that altitude/height until overflying the 'ME' locator which, in the elevation section, has the letters LOM (co-sited Locator and Outer Marker transmitters). Note the frequencies of these two NDBs because, after overflying 'MCR', the ADF receiver will have to be changed from 388 to 396 KHz.

12. While flying outbound both the middle and the outer marker beacons will code. After overflying the LOM (i.e. the 'ME' Locator) a descent is made through 250 ft on a heading of 058°. This heading is held for 1 minute after crossing the LOM assuming a speed of less than 150 kt (left-hand panel and Note 4).

13. Note the cross below MCT 8d. This is the symbol for a **Final Approach Fix**, the starting point of the approach. The letters and figures above the symbol mean that the aircraft will be at the final approach fix when the DME (IDENT letters MCT) reads 8 n.m. **At present not every ILS installation includes DME and it is not essential to the procedure.**

14. Assuming an approach ground speed of 80 kt, rate of descent should be 420 ft/min. and from the LOM to the threshold will take 2 min. 47 sec. (left-hand panel).

15. Note the missed approach procedure which entails climbing straight ahead to the 'MCR' beacon then turning left into the hold. The climb must be continued until 3000 ft QNH (2750 ft QFE).

16. Study notes 2 to 5 in the centre panel. Notes 1 and 6 relate to the LLZ/DME procedure (localizer only combined with DME) which is not described in this chapter.

Descent and Approach to Decision Height

All the usual preliminaries previously described for the other aids apply to ILS. Manchester ATIS (explained in Chapter 9, page 159) will provide Golf Alpha Bravo Charlie Delta with:

Airfield information
Airfield weather
Runway in use
QNH and QFE (which, as always, must be noted)

At airfields without ATIS facilities the information will be obtained on the approach frequency.

After a ten minute hold on the BARTON VOR/DME at FL50 the aircraft is cleared to approach the 'MCR' beacon. Its frequency would have been selected in anticipation since this is the starting fix for the procedure. While flying towards it on the 168° radial FROM BARTON Manchester instruct the pilot to descend to 3000 QNH. The pilot must report established on the 168 radial from Barton and, on arrival at the new altitude, "level at three thousand feet".

While heading to the 'MCR' beacon the ILS frequency (109.5 MHz) will be selected and the IDENT checked (letters I – NN) so that the localizer needle may be used to maintain the runway QDR while flying outbound.

1. When the 'over-the-beacon' signal is given on the ADF turn LEFT to intercept the 058° outbound heading. This will entail continuing the turn to 058° – 15° = 043° (plus or minus drift) in order to regain the 058° Tr. (M) to the LOM. While flying towards the LOM:

    (a) Select 396 (the LOM frequency) on the ADF.
    (b) Trim the aircraft at circuit speed and complete the pre-landing vital actions.
    (c) Check the ILS IDENT and, if it is to be used, the IDENT of the MCT DME.
    (d) Check the altimeter setting(s).

NOTE: It should be understood that, if circumstances demand, ATC can vary the procedure. For example, the aircraft could have arrived over the 'MCR' beacon and started to fly towards the procedure turn. A delay or inadequate separation from traffic ahead might cause ATC to place Golf Charlie Delta in the hold based on the 'ME' beacon.

In this example the procedure is allowed to continue without delay.

2. If DME is being used range should be decreasing as the aircraft flies from the 'MCR' beacon towards overhead the runway threshold but since it will pass overhead at 2750 ft agl the lowest DME reading will be 0.5 n.m.

3. Soon after overflying the runway threshold the middle marker will code, the localizer will be giving "FLY LEFT"/"FLY RIGHT" commands (but in the reverse sense because the aircraft is heading in the opposite direction to the approach) and the glidepath needle will be showing a maximum "FLY DOWN" indication. By now drift will have been found and this will be of assistance during the approach.

4. Although the ILS is giving reverse commands it should be used to maintain the correct outbound leg in conjunction with the ADF which is now pointing to the 'ME' beacon.

5. As the NDB is approached the outer marker will be heard, gradually becoming louder until the ADF gives the 'over-the-beacon' signal. The outer marker light will by then be flashing to indicate 'overhead-the-marker' and at that point:
   (a) Start the watch.
   (b) Commence a descent to 2750 ft QNH (2500 ft QFE). Since only 250 ft must be lost rate of descent is not critical.

6. One minute after overflying the LOM turn onto 013° (plus or minus the previously found drift allowance) and start the procedure turn. In this example an approach *groundspeed* of 80 kt is suitable for the aircraft and since the reported wind is 220°/25 kt there will be little drift but to achieve the correct groundspeed an IAS of 105 kt must be flown. Note this speed on the pad.

7. Fly the 013° leg for 45 seconds, then start a Rate 1 turn to the right, gradually closing with the extended runway centreline. From this point the ILS will be the prime reference. Stop and zero the watch. If the DI is within a few degrees of the 238° QDM and the localizer needle is indicating a maximum FLY LEFT reduce or even stop the turn until it moves towards the centre. If the localizer needle moves from maximum FLY LEFT, through the centre to FLY RIGHT, the aircraft has flown through the extended runway centreline and the turn should be continued to centre the needle before settling on a Hdg (M) or 238° +/− drift correction. Intercepting the localizer is illustrated in Fig. 42.

8. Place the aircraft in the landing configuration and trim it at the correct airspeed, in this case 105 kt. At this stage the glidepath needle will be indicating maximum FLY UP. Gradually the

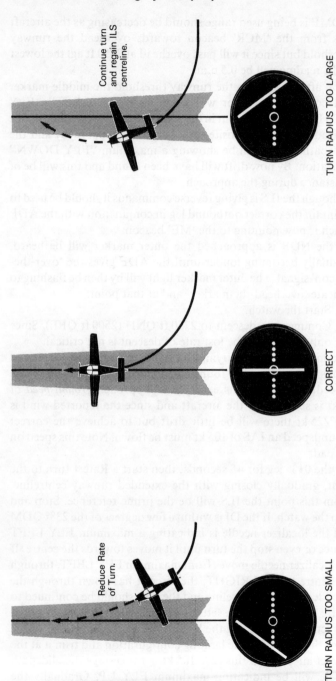

Fig. 42   Using the Localizer needle to determine proximity of the Extended Runway Centreline and corrections to be adopted while turning onto the approach.

needle will move down its scale and as it approaches the centre of the instrument reduce power and start a 420 ft/min. rate of descent. When DME is being used as an additional aid the needle will indicate ON THE GLIDEPATH when 8 n.m. is shown on the distance readout *provided* the aircraft is at 2750 ft QNH.

Responding to ILS Commands

Although ILS is a very accurate aid, which portrays small departures from extended runway centreline and glidepath by large needle movements, it is nevertheless easy to use provided certain basic rules are observed. These are:

- The ILS needles provide *commands*, namely —

    > FLY UP
    > ON THE GLIDEPATH
    > FLY DOWN
    > FLY LEFT
    > ON THE CENTRELINE
    > FLY RIGHT.

- Headings are steered with reference to the direction indicator, *not* the ILS instrument.

- Control of aircraft attitude, speed, balance, etc., must be made with reference to the flight instruments in the normal way. The ILS does not replace these instruments; **where the needles cross is where the aircraft should be** and the controls must be used to fly the circle in the centre of the dial to that cross.

- The slightest departure from centre of either needle must provoke an immediate reaction. On no account allow an attitude of 'it will be all right' to encourage inertia in the hope that the situation will improve. Most likely it will become worse unless corrective action is taken.

- To maintain the extended runway centreline make *small* heading corrections until the needle settles within the little circle. Note the heading. The difference between it and the runway QDM represents drift.

- The aircraft must be accurately trimmed at the correct approach speed with sufficient power to maintain the required rate of descent.

    While in principle the 'speed-with-elevator/descent-rate-with-power' concept remains true while flying an ILS it should be remembered that a maximum FLY UP signal means the aircraft is at least 0.75° below the glidepath and a maximum FLY DOWN indicates a departure of only 0.45° or more above. Such small departures from glidepath are best dealt with by raising or lowering the nose with the elevators.

A persistent overshoot or undershoot tendency, although the airspeed is correct, will naturally require a change in power setting.

Descent to Decision Height

The aircraft has arrived on the centreline and a 420 ft/min. rate of descent has been set up as the glidepath needle moves down the instrument dial and centres.

9. Constantly check the ILS needles but not to the exclusion of the other instruments. If the localizer moves to either side of centre turn slightly in the direction indicated and fly the circle to the needle which should be regarded as the extended runway centreline.

10. If the glidepath needle moves up or down in relation to the circle move the elevators in the same direction and fly the circle to the needle which should be regarded as the plane of the glidepath.

    If the airspeed is correct but the aircraft tends to climb reduce power slightly and re-trim. A constant undershoot situation should be dealt with by adding power slightly and re-trimming at the correct airspeed. Minor, short term departures from glidepath should be dealt with on the elevators as described.

11. If DME is being used check progress towards the threshold. Four n.m. from the runway the outer marker will be heard, gradually increasing in volume until the marker light flashes. At the same time the ADF will give the usual 'over-the-beacon' signal because it is sited along with the marker transmitter. Start the watch and call "Manchester Approach, Golf Charlie Delta outer marker inbound".

    ATC will give landing clearance at this point.

12. Provided the aircraft is on the glidepath at the beacon, height should be 1220 ft QFE and this should be checked on the altimeter. According to the left-hand table, from the LOM to the threshold will take 2 min. 47 sec. at a groundspeed of 80 kt.

    Decision height is 420 ft, representing a descent from 1220 ft at the LOM through 800 ft. Reference to the height/distance table on page 145 shows that, assuming a 3° glidepath, at 420 ft the aircraft will be about 1¼ n.m. from the threshold, i.e. shortly before reaching the middle marker (an Instrument Rated pilot using a 220 ft DH would by that height have overflown the marker).

13. At 500 ft the aircraft breaks cloud into poor visibility with a few ground features coming into view. Continue flying the ILS to decision height and, if by then visual contact has not been established to the point where a visual approach can continue, carry out a missed approach.

On this occasion ground features are becoming clearer as the middle marker codes. Soon afterwards the approach lights come into view and the pilot can continue with a visual approach and landing.

Missed Approach/Visual Manoeuvring

In the above example the transition from instrument to visual flight was made shortly before descending to decision height. Had the ground remained obscured, or had visual contact been poor to the point where ground features could not be recognized, power would have been added just before reaching 420 ft and the following missed approach procedure would have been flown:

1. Advise Manchester Tower that missed approach action is being taken.
2. Maintain the present heading and climb straight ahead.
3. Change ADF frequency to 388 KHz to receive the upwind locator, identify the letters MCR and maintain the 238° QDM with reference to the ADF and DI.
4. On overflying the MCR Locator turn left and enter the hold. If necessary continue climbing and level out at 3000 ft QNH (2750 ft QFE).
5. Prepare for another approach or divert according to circumstances.

Visual Manoeuvring

The AERODROME OPERATING MINIMA page for Manchester International gives a decision height of 650 ft for all circling when the aircraft is propeller driven and not exceeding 5700 kg MTWA. This is somewhat higher than the 420 ft decision height calculated for an ILS approach flown by an IMC rated pilot because ILS is a precision approach capable of positioning the aircraft accurately relative to the centreline and the glidepath.

It could be that at some airfields the ILS is confined to one runway while wind conditions demand landing on another. In this case ILS would be used to break cloud and establish visual contact with the ground so that a circling approach to the runway could be made while keeping the airfield in view. The aircraft should be flown at low safe cruising speed. If the cause of circling was mis-alignment with the runway during the final stages of an ILS approach, making it necessary to circle for a visual landing with the airfield in sight, the ILS should be used to assist in lining up with the runway.

When a commitment has been made to fly visually it is essential to maintain a good lookout. The ILS should be regarded as a precision aid to aligning with the runway and attaining the correct glidepath. The equipment can be relied upon to perform its task and when an ILS approach fails this is usually caused by the weak link in the chain — the pilot.

CONCLUSIONS

ILS is, on its own, an easy to use, precision approach aid which allows relatively high landing rates in poor weather. When ILS is used in conjunction with an airfield-located DME giving constant distance-to-threshold information there is an added degree of precision although the main value of this growing practice is when, for any reason, the glidepath transmitter is not available due to maintenance or when the aircraft has VOR but no ILS equipment.

ILS will eventually be replaced by the Microwave Landing System (MLS) which is expected to offer a number of advantages over existing equipment, mainly in terms of more flexible approach path requirements.

Chapter 8
Surveillance Radar Approaches (SRA)

This chapter deals with radar as an approach aid. Ground equipment designed for aviation use, which is described in Chapter 11, may be:

(a) **Precision Approach Radar (PAR)** which is, in the main, confined to military airfields, and

(b) **Surveillance Radar Element (SRE)**, a simpler installation in widespread civil use. While SRE is less accurate than PAR it is nevertheless capable of positioning aircraft within close limits.

Prime uses of SRE

The term 'Surveillance Approach Radar' applies when SRE is used to guide an aircraft making a part circuit and approach. However, the equipment is a valuable general purpose tool of air traffic control. Typical functions of SRA are:

1. Providing air traffic separation within and outside controlled airspace.
2. Sequencing aircraft approaching busy airports to ensure safety while providing a rapid landing rate in poor weather.
3. Vectoring aircraft onto the ILS localizer (described in Chapter 7) or other approach aids.
4. Radar monitoring of ILS approaches.
5. Radar control of departing aircraft.
6. Guiding an aircraft on a radar approach.

To ensure vertical separation the controller must know the altitude/flight level of all aircraft flying within the radar area and this essential information will be provided by:

(i) An **Encoding Altimeter** passing information through the aircraft's **Transponder** (described in Chapter 11) or, when this equipment is not installed,

(ii) Pilot reports passed over the RTF.

Radar Identification

In so far as the pilot is concerned identification of the radar service is a matter of selecting the correct frequency and establishing normal RTF contact with the radar service required. Unlike the other radio aids described in previous chapters successful operation of SRA depends upon the ground station identifying the aircraft from among the many other echoes that may appear on the screen at the same time. Identification is accomplished by:

(i) Setting the transponder code passed to the pilot by the radar controller or, when such facilities are not available on the ground or in the aircraft,

(ii) Turning the aircraft at the request of the radar controller so that its echo may be identified.

Use of SSR (Secondary Surveillance Radar)

To enhance the strength of aircraft echoes on the radar screen, an important factor when rain or other 'clutter' is present, and to provide positive aircraft identification without need of turning onto a new heading, many radar stations are able to accept coded signals from a transponder carried in the aircraft. As explained in Chapter 11 (page 231) the transponder can be selected to any one of 4096 four-figure codes and whatever numbers are set on the equipment will appear on the radar operator's screen adjacent to the aircraft echo. When an encoding altimeter (page 231) is carried the echo will also include altitude at intervals of 100 ft.

Some transponders require a warm-up period of almost one minute before they will function and it is therefore important to switch on the equipment before take-off. However, like all avionics, to prevent possible damage from current surge the transponder must not be switched on during engine starting.

When the controller wishes to receive transponder echoes on a particular code (to identify the echo from those of other aircraft) the pilot will, for example, be requested to:

'Squawk four seven zero zero'

Before setting the numbers **4 7 0 0** (or whatever numbers are requested) on the transponder the function switch should be moved to SBY (standby) otherwise a series of numbers will clutter the radar operator's screen while the equipment is being adjusted. Only after the code has been set should the switch be returned to ON or, when an encoding altimeter is fitted, the ALT position.

Confirmation that the transponder is being interrogated will be provided by the reply light which will flash at intervals of approximately 10–15 seconds unless it is responding to several ground stations simultaneously when the light will flicker almost continuously.

When further confirmation of identity is required the radar controller will call:

'Golf Charlie Delta squawk ident'.

This is a request for echo enhancement; the echo and its accompanying code numbers will glow more brightly on the radar screen while the IDENT facility is operated in the aircraft. IDENT may be selected on the function switch or, on some transponders, with a small pushbutton.

For the type of flying likely to be conducted by IMC-rated pilots it is not essential that a transponder should be carried to make use of the various radar services. However, it is a mandatory requirement for aircraft making use of the airways system.

Use of SRE

Being a ground interpreted aid SRE is very easy to use in the air. Whatever the service required — advisory (e.g. separation from other traffic outside controlled airspace), vectoring onto a VOR/NDB/ILS, or radar approach, etc. — the sequence of events is as follows:

1. Select the required service, find its radio frequency in the AERAD Supplement or the relevant chart and set this on the transceiver.
2. Call the station, e.g. 'Birmingham Radar', 'Heathrow Radar', etc. and ask for the service required.
3. When a transponder is to be used set the codes and 'Squawk' as requested by the controller.
4. Follow instructions passed by the radar controller.

Radar controllers are trained to present instructions and information in a calm manner that is particularly reassuring to the inexperienced pilot.

Advisory Service

A valuable form of assistance provided by SRE, for example in poor visibility when separation from other aircraft can become a matter of concern, is the Advisory Service. This is of particular value while transiting areas of heavy air traffic which are outside controlled airspace.

Some of the airspaces served by SRE are called **Advisory Service Areas** and **Advisory Service Routes**. They are so designated because, although subject to relatively heavy traffic, they do not warrant the establishment of full Control Area/Airway status.

Typical messages passed by the radar controller would be:

'Golf Charlie Delta there is traffic in your eleven o'clock position moving from south to north, altitude unknown [which might be the case if the 'unknown' aircraft was not using a transponder with an encoding altimeter]', or

'Golf Charlie Delta turn left onto a heading of two-five-zero degrees to avoid other traffic'.

It should be understood that advisory service areas and routes are not controlled airspace and pilots are therefore under no obligation to use the services provided. Nevertheless their effectiveness very much depends on the cooperation of pilots flying in the area. There are the obvious advantages of protection from other, often unseen traffic and the provision of heading guidance in the absence of suitably located VORs or NDBs.

To make use of the advisory service areas or routes a flight plan should be filed at least ten minutes before departure. However this requirement need not prevent a pilot from seeking the assistance of radar at any time.

Pilots wishing to make use of the UK Lower Airspace Radar Service (LARS) described in Chapter 9 should make contact with the Royal Air Force station providing the required service when the aircraft is within 30 n.m.

The SRA let-down and approach

Airfields equipped with SRE will, as previously mentioned, provide radar-monitored transit through the area, vectoring onto the approach aid (ILS, NDB, VOR) or SRA (Surveillance Radar Approach). In such cases a RADAR VECTORING AREA chart will be published and an example (GLASGOW) is shown in Fig. 43.

The **Radar Vectoring Area** is shown on these charts along with the following information:

1. Minimum altitudes to be allocated by the radar controller (in this

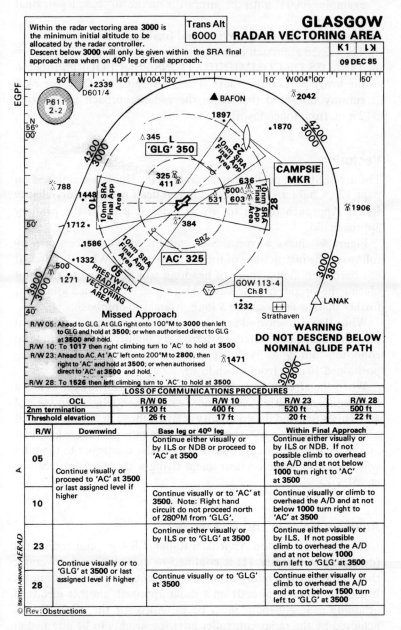

Fig. 43   Radar Vectoring Area Chart (*by kind permission of AERAD*).

example, 3000 ft until the aircraft is on the 40° base leg or final approach).
2. The runways, their centrelines and final approach areas.
3. The missed approach instructions for each runway.
4. The LOSS OF COMMUNICATIONS PROCEDURES listed in the lower part of the chart. These also give the OCL for each runway threshold (based on the radar approach terminating 2 n.m. from touchdown).

Vectoring

The use of SRE to position an aircraft on the ILS was mentioned on page 126, Chapter 7. The following text deals with the Surveillance Radar Approach (SRA) in which radar is used as the primary approach aid.

Figure 44 shows a typical SRA pattern which will be flown by following the instructions of the radar controller. When the aircraft has been identified a series of headings will be passed to the pilot placing the aircraft on a downwind leg which is continued somewhat further than usual to ensure a long, straight-in approach.

While flying downwind at circuit speed the usual pre-landing vital actions must be completed. Patterns vary slightly according to local conditions but typically the aircraft will be turned onto a base leg positioned 10 n.m. from touchdown.

When the aircraft is within 10° of extended runway centreline a heading change will be given to close with the centreline at an angle of 40°. This is to avoid the possibility of flying through the QDM that is often present during a 90° turn. Throughout the procedure headings and other instructions are passed from radar controller to the pilot who can concentrate on instrument flying without need of reading charts, etc.

Advisory Heights and Distances

Unlike PAR (Precision Approach Radar) SRA ground equipment (described in Chapter 11) is confined to providing area coverage; there is no glidepath information. Consequently, when the equipment is used to guide an aircraft on a radar approach another means of attaining a 3° glidepath must be provided for the pilot. This is achieved by the radar controller advising heights to be attained at intervals of one mile until 2 n.m. from touchdown, at which point the procedure ends. The final approach and landing must then continue visually or, if visual contact has not been established, missed approach action will be taken.

The following table of heights to be achieved while descending on a 3° glidepath applies to all approaches and some of the key figures (e.g. 6 n.m., 4 n.m., and 2 n.m.) are worth remembering.

Distance from touchdown	Height to fly 3° glidepath
8 n.m.	2450 ft
7 n.m.	2150 ft
6 n.m.	1850 ft
5 n.m.	1550 ft
4 n.m.	1250 ft
3 n.m.	950 ft
2 n.m.	650 ft
SRA terminates at this point.	
1½ n.m.	500 ft
1 n.m.	350 ft

Descent to Termination/Decision Height

In this example Golf Alpha Bravo Charlie Delta has contacted Fairfield Radar and requested a radar approach. The radar controller has responded with:

Airfield information
Airfield weather
Runway in use (in this case 'runway three-four')
QNH and QFE which are noted and read back.

The following procedure should be studied in conjunction with Fig. 44:

1. *Fairfield Radar* 'Golf Charlie Delta maintain two thousand five hundred feet. This will be a surveillance radar approach

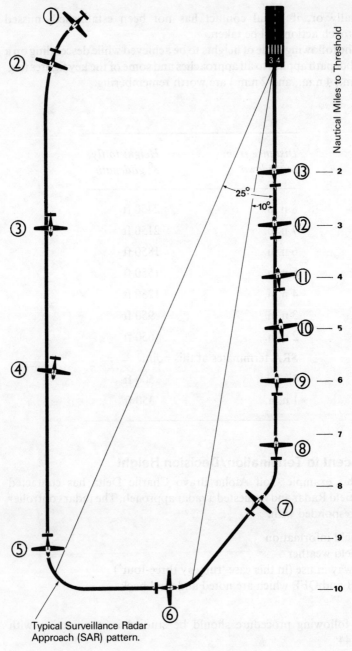

Typical Surveillance Radar Approach (SAR) pattern.

Fig. 44 Typical circuit pattern adopted while flying a Surveillance Radar Approach (numbers relate to the procedure described in the text).

terminating two miles from touchdown. Obstacle clearance limit three-eight-zero feet. Check your minima.'

Decision height = 380 + 50 = 430 ft for an I/R pilot.
+ 200 ft = 630 ft for an IMC pilot.

NOTE: Reference to the height/distance table on page 145 shows that at 2 n.m. from touchdown (the termination point for this procedure) the aircraft should be at 650 ft which is slightly above DH.

2. *Fairfield Radar* 'Golf Charlie Delta turn left heading one-six-zero.'

3. 'Golf Charlie Delta your position five miles south west of Fairfield on a downwind leg.'
Pre-landing vital actions should now be completed with the aircraft trimmed at circuit speed.

4. 'Golf Charlie Delta your position seven miles south west of Fairfield. Turn right five degrees.'
(This is to counter left drift).

5. 'Golf Charlie Delta your position ten miles from Fairfield turn left heading zero-seven-zero degrees for a left-hand base leg.'
(Speed should now be reduced and approach flap applied).

6. 'Golf Charlie Delta turn left heading zero-two-zero degrees. Descend to two thousand five hundred feet, QNH xxxx millibars.'
(This heading will intercept the centreline at an angle of 40°).

7. 'Golf Charlie Delta you are closing with the centreline turn left onto three-four-zero degrees.'
(At this stage the aircraft will be on long finals flying level at a altitude of 2500 ft).

8. 'Range coming up to seven miles. Golf Charlie Delta is cleared to land, QFE xxxx, surface wind xxx,xx knots. Commence your descent to maintain a three degree glidepath. Check wheels down and locked. Do not acknowledge further instructions.'
(At this point a descent down the glidepath is commenced).

9. 'Range six miles. Height should be one thousand eight hundred and fifty feet.'
(If during stages 9, 10, 11 or 12 the aircraft is above or below the height given by the radar controller rate of descent must be adjusted).

10. 'Range five miles. Height should be one thousand five hundred and fifty feet. Slightly to the right of centreline; turn left five degrees'.

11. 'Range four miles. Height should be one thousand two hundred and fifty feet. Closing with the centreline.'

12. 'Range three miles. Height should be nine hundred and fifty feet. On the centreline alter heading two degrees right.'
(The 2° heading adjustment is necessary to prevent flying through the centreline).

13. 'Range two miles. Height should be six hundred and fifty feet. Radar Approach completed.'

Provided visual contact has been established the approach and landing may continue. If, for any reason (e.g. misalignment with the runway), it is not possible to continue the landing missed approach action will have to be taken.

The example described above entailed flying a near-standard circuit but Radar may adopt different patterns according to circumstances.

Missed Approach/Visual Manoeuvring

Like any other instrument approach, if visual contact with the ground has not been made by decision height power must be added immediately and the prescribed missed approach action commenced. The missed approach procedure will be described on the RADAR VECTORING AREA chart. Often it entails climbing towards an NDB followed by a hold but the radar controller will be able to render assistance, for example, if it is decided to make another radar approach without delay.

Visual Manoeuvring

If, following a radar approach the aircraft breaks cloud but alignment with the runway is not good enough to ensure a safe landing it may be possible to circle within sight of the airfield and position for a visual approach. Published circling limits for the airfield (Decision Height and Visibility/RVR) must be complied with and radar may be in a position to offer assistance while positioning for another approach.

Precision Approach Radar (PAR)

PAR equipment is mainly confined to military or joint civil/military airfields but since a civil pilot in urgent need of assistance during poor weather may be directed to such a unit this chapter is concluded with a brief explanation of how the procedure differs from the SRA previously described.

Since PAR embodies a second screen depicting glidepath information the radar controller is presented with two pictures:

1. Aircraft progress along the extended runway centreline.

2. Aircraft progress down the glidepath.

Since departures from centreline and/or glidepath are shown on a continuous basis the radar controller is able to provide very accurate guidance and a PAR procedure is continued until $\frac{1}{2}$ n.m. from touchdown. At that stage the aircraft will obviously be lower than at the 2 n.m. termination point for SRA.

As PAR is a precision aid the radar controller will report progress at half-mile intervals during the final approach (SAR reports are at intervals of 1 nm). During the SAR procedure previously explained the radar controller made such calls as:

'Range three miles. Height should be nine hundred and fifty feet.'

A PAR controller would say:

'Range three miles. On the glidepath' or '— slightly above the glidepath. Increase your rate of descent' as the case may be.

In so far as the pilot is concerned flying techniques are the same for either procedure, SAR or PAR, the advantage of PAR being greater accuracy and therefore its ability to continue tracking the aircraft to within $\frac{1}{2}$ n.m. of touchdown. Many of the skilled RAF radar controllers can, if necessary, talk an aircraft onto the runway but naturally this demands matching skill of the pilot flying the approach and appropriate qualifications.

Ground Studies

Chapter 9

Summary of ATC and Meteorological Services

Air Traffic Control and some of the legal aspects that apply are outlined on pages 9 to 27, *Flight Briefing for Pilots, Volume 2*. However, while flying in IMC there is an enhanced relationship between the pilot and the controlling authorities; close co-operation is essential in the interest of safe flight and adequate separation from other traffic.

During IMC flight the pilot will be transferred from one control/advisory service to another and it therefore follows that knowing of the existence of these services is, in itself, not enough; pilots should try and gain practical experience of their use. Air law and the limits/position of controlled airspace are constantly changing, consequently in a book of this nature it is only possible to present a general picture of the ATC and meteorology organisations. Much of the information is in summary form because most of it has already been covered in Volumes 1 and 2 of the *Flight Briefing for Pilots* series.

The following subjects should be revised during the IMC Rating course:

Visual flight rules	(pages 9–10, Volume 2)
Altimeter setting procedures	(pages 120–123, Volume 2)
Horizontal pressure changes	(pages 123–126, Volume 2)
Radio failure	(pages 23 and 63, CAP 413)

Aeronautical Information Service

The following publications are available to pilots:

Air Information Publication (CAP 32)

These volumes, which are kept up-to-date by an amendment service, are strongly recommended to IMC rated pilots who plan to use an aircraft for more serious purposes than pleasure flying. Their size is more formidable than the contents which are clearly presented. CAP 32 is divided into these sections:

GEN General AGA (Aerodromes).
COM Communications and MET (Meteorology).
RAC Air traffic rules and services.
FAL Facilitation of SAR (Search and Rescue).
MAP Aeronautical charts.

NOTAMS

These Notices to Airmen are used to supplement the *Air Information Publication.* They usually convey information of a temporary nature but when the notice is permanent it will eventually be incorporated within the AIP. NOTAMS are published as required and numbered consecutively throughout the year.

Aeronautical Information Circulars

These circulars are issued weekly by the UK Civil Aviation Authority, their purpose being to notify administration and operational matters. They can be obtained from The Aeronautical Information Service, Tolcarne Drive, Pinner, Middlesex HA5 2DU.

Air Traffic Services

The organization of air traffic control is, in most respects, standard throughout the world although there are some differences in detail. Airspace is designated under the following headings:

Flight Information Regions (FIRs)
Control Zones
Control Areas
Airways
Advisory Service Areas
Advisory Routes
Special Rules Area/Zone
Military Airfield Traffic Zones (MATZ)
Danger/Restricted/Prohibited Areas.

The purpose of these elements of the ATC system and the services provided by them is explained on pages 10 to 16 of *Flight Briefing for Pilots, Volume 2.* Although the subject of ATC is dealt with at PPL level in Volume 2 the following additional information will be of value to pilots studying for an IMC rating.

UK Lower Airspace Radar Service (LARS)

Much of the UK enjoys radar coverage provided by some 30 Royal Air Force stations for aircraft flying outside controlled airspace up to and including FL95. The navigational assistance provided by this widespread radar coverage is additional to the various services offered by the civil ATS (Air Traffic Control Service). Some stations operate on a 24-hour basis, others are restricted to the following hours, Monday to Friday:

Summer 0700 to 1600 hrs.
Winter 0800 to 1700 hrs.

Hours of operation and station frequencies are published in the *Air Information Publication* and the AERAD Supplement.

Aeronautical Information Service (AIS)

Central to the planning of all flights, particularly those likely to be conducted in IMC, is the collation of facts. Only when the facts are known can a pilot consider the options before selecting routes, radio facilities, alternates, etc. Without knowing the facts it is impossible to plan the flight, whether or not a flight plan must be filed.

At some of the larger airfields flight planning assistance is available, either in the form of a flight planning office or 'self briefing' facilities which, although not staffed, will provide advice via a direct telephone line. In some cases the weather conditions will require **Special VFR Clearance** and demand of the pilot an IMC Rating.

Airspace Restrictions

Airways, Terminal Control Areas (TMA) and Control Zones (CTR) operate under permanent Rule 21 conditions, i.e. Instrument Flight Rules (IFR) are in operation at all times, day and night, regardless of weather conditions.

Some airfields have a **Special Rules Zone,** which extends from ground level to a published height, or a **Special Rules Area** starting at a prescribed height and extending to an upper limit. Within this airspace pilots are required to:

(a) Maintain a listening watch on the designated frequency.
(b) Notify ATC of position, track and altitude/flight level.
(c) Remain 1 n.m. horizontally and 1000 ft vertically from cloud. IMC-rated pilots may fly in an SRZ/SRA provided there is a flight visibility of at least 1½ n.m.

Special VFR Clearances

At the busier airfields aircraft flown by pilots with an IMC Rating will be given a Special VFR Clearance (SVFR) provided the weather remains within the limits of that qualification (minimum flight visibility of 1 n.m. below cloud or 1.5 n.m. above. Pilots without an IMC Rating must remain within sight of the ground and have a minimum flight visibility of 5 n.m.).

Whereas the instrument-rated pilot will use Standard Arrival Charts (STARs) and Standard Instrument Departure Charts (SIDs) those with a PPL/IMC rating will be expected to comply with specified **Entry/Exit Lanes** and during the flight planning stage it is essential that the pilot should understand their location. For this purpose VFR Charts are published and an example is shown in Fig. 45. The charts include a number of reporting points and to assist in their location radials from suitable VORs are given.

Prohibited, Restricted, Danger and Special Areas

Some airspace is subject to various degrees of restriction. The areas are:

Danger Area. Such areas may be used for weapons training, target towing and other military purposes. On AERAD charts they are shown as follows —

Permanent (restricted at all times). Broken blue outline.
Notified (restricted at certain times). Solid blue outline.

A letter and numbers within the area contained in solid or broken lines may be referred to the title page of the AERAD Radio Navigation Chart which gives upper and lower limits of the danger area and hours of operation when it is 'Notified'. Details may be obtained in flight by calling the **Danger Area Activity Information Service (DAAIS)** on the appropriate RTF frequency which is listed under that heading in the AERAD Supplement.

Prohibited Area. These areas, through/over which aircraft must not fly, may cover land or territorial water. They are shown on AERAD charts as shaded areas.

Restricted Area. The purpose of these areas is to restrict aircraft because of non-security considerations (e.g. to prevent flight over a bird sanctuary). Method of chart presentation is the same as for danger areas.

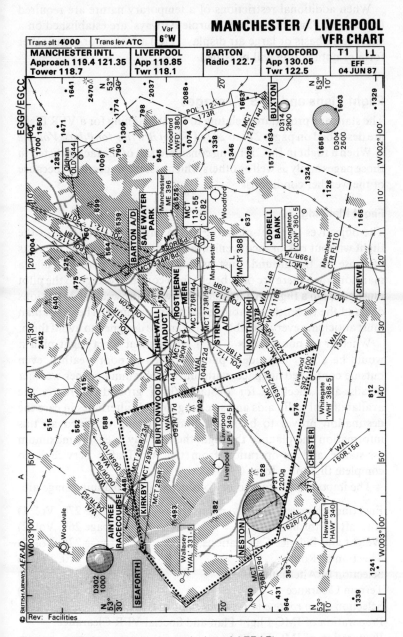

Fig. 45   VFR Chart (*by kind permission of AERAD*).

When additional restrictions of a temporary nature are required (e.g. Royal Flights for which 'Purple Airways' are established on a short-term basis or large air displays, etc.) a Notam or some other form of notification will be issued.

Flight Plans and ATS Messages

The standard procedures relating to flight planning for a VFR flight are described on pages 270 to 282 of *Flight Briefing for Pilots, Volume 1*. When a flight in IMC is being considered all of the factors listed in those pages apply as well as others which assume importance because of the weather conditions.

Flight Planning

The objectives of flight planning are to ensure safe conduct of the flight without risk or inconvenience to other traffic and the interests of those on the ground. Just as one should not plan to build a mansion when there are only bricks for a country cottage so the pilot must not plan a flight in a light aircraft when the weather conditions demand the technical capabilities of a large airliner. The flight plan must anticipate every possible hazard and be designed to avoid them.

Whether or not there is a legal requirement for a flight plan it would be a very imprudent pilot who flew in poor weather, even outside controlled airspace, without first obtaining proper weather details and checking for obstacles/high ground *en route*, the availability of radio aids and selecting suitable alternates in case the destination proves to be below limits. Having obtained all this information and planned the flight the best way to ensure maximum assistance and co-operation from the Air Traffic Service is to complete flightplan form CA 48.

The important factors to be considered at the planning stage are:

Fuel (including reserves/diversions)	(page 278, Vol. 1)
Aircraft Performance	(page 269, Vol. 2)
Weight and Balance Calculations	(page 276, Vol. 2)
Selection of Route	(page 270, Vol. 1)
Selection of Alternates	(page 273, Vol. 1)
Terrain Clearance	(page 271, Vol. 1)

Selection of *en route and terminal radio aids*.
Preparation of IMC Flight Plan and Special VFR Clearance.
Preparation of IMC Flight Log.

Suitable flight log forms are available from most aviation suppliers.

ATS Messages

Chapter 10, 'Introduction to Radiotelephony' in *Flight Briefing for Pilots, Volume 2* explains the terminology and various procedures used in aeronautical communications.

At some of the more important airfields an **Automatic Terminal Information Service (ATIS)** is transmitted over the voice channel of a suitably located VOR or a TVOR (Terminal VOR) at the aerodrome. The information, which is constantly up-dated, will be preceded by a code name (e.g. Alpha, Bravo, etc.).

Pilots approaching a destination operating an ATIS should note the information and on first contact with Approach Control confirm it has been received with the words: 'Information Alpha [or whatever the code being used] received.'

The following information for arriving aircraft may be included in an ATIS transmission:

Traffic pattern information
Type of instrument approach to be expected
Runway in use
Surface wind
Cloud base and visibility
Altimeter settings
Airfield conditions.

Departing aircraft will receive:
Runway in use
Surface wind
Altimeter settings.

Meteorological Services

Contact with the met office should entail more than obtaining the local wind and a brief encounter with the TAFs (Terminal Aerodrome Forecasts). Essential information required at the flight planning stage is comprehensive, even for a SVFR flight as these questions will reveal:

1. Are there any fronts across or near the proposed route and, if so, what will be their effect on flight conditions?
2. Will the wind back, veer, decrease or increase?
3. How will the cloud vary in amount, type and vertical extent? What are the expected ceilings *en route* and the reported ceilings at the destination and alternate(s)?

4. What will be the visibility, *en route* and at the destination or alternate(s)?
5. Will there be port or starboard drift and how will this affect safety height due to the altimeter over or under-reading (page 123, Volume 2 of this series)?
6. When high ground is to be overflown will there be risks from turbulence, up/down draughts, wave cycles, etc.?
7. It would be the height of folly to attempt a flight in an aircraft without proper ice protection when icing conditions exist. So what are the icing risks for this flight?

At the Destination

The weather may be quite good at the point of departure, it may be within the competence of the pilot during the flight but conditions at the destination are also important. Before deciding whether or not to make the flight the pilot will want to know:

1. Visibility and cloudbase at the destination.
2. Wind strength and the presence of any weather.
3. Icing risk.
4. Availability of radar/radio aids and the unserviceability of any equipment that might be important in marginal weather conditions.
5. **Tempo**, the weather tendency over the next few hours. Because even if the weather at the destination is within limits at time of departure a lot can change during the flight. Temperature and dew point will obviously interest the pilot because when they are close a falling temperature could lead to fog (page 89, Volume 2 of this series). **Remember, weather forecasts are time-related — they are not valid forever.**

Sources of Met Information

Meteorology is covered in adequate detail for the PPL/IMC Rating in Chapter 3 of *Flight Briefing for Pilots, Volume 2*. The weather forecast is dealt with on pages 103 to 113 of the same book (along with examples of the various forms used by the Meteorological Service) and the practical aspects of meteorology are explained in pages 113 to 126. Students for the IMC Rating are strongly recommended to revise this text.

While a good knowledge of meteorology is essential in the interest of effective flight planning, knowing how and where to obtain the information during the planning stage and while in flight is also important. These various sources are now listed:

AIRMET Service

A UK low level met forecast and aerodrome weather information service covering the UK up to 15,000 ft (winds up to 18,000 ft). Information is updated four times daily and amended more frequently as required.

Forecasts covering the period 0545 to 2300 are recorded but at other times information may be passed over the telephone by a met officer. For maximum convenience the information should be taken down on Pilot's Proforma CA1701 which also shows the area covered and relevant telephone numbers on the reverse side.

AIRMET is described on page 105 of *Flight Briefing for Pilots, Volume 2* and the Pilot's Proforma is illustrated in Figs. 44 and 45 of that volume.

Forecast Weather below 15,000 ft

The met office at London (Heathrow) Airport prepares UK low level area and route forecasts for onward transmission to other airfields equipped with automatic printout machines. The information is presented in pictorial and tabular form but further information and clarification may be obtained at major airfields with their own met office.

Meteorological Aerodrome Reports (METAR)

These reports, which are 'actuals' describing present weather conditions at the airfield, are distributed in METAR code (an example is shown on page 105, Volume 2 of this series) or verbally in plain language.

Terminal Aerodrome Forecasts (TAF)

Whereas METARs are reports of current weather conditions at an airfield TAFs are forecasts covering a specified period.

Examples of the various met forms are shown in Chapter 3 of *Flight Briefing for Pilots, Volume 2.*

VOLMET

In the air, and on the ground when within range of the transmitter, current weather reports for the principal airports are broadcast on VHF frequencies from major airports throughout the world. For example, in the UK the following airport weather is transmitted on a continuous basis (the frequencies quoted were correct as at February, 1987):

Service Ident	Frequency	Airports Reported
'London VOLMET Main'	135.375	Heathrow, Gatwick, Birmingham, Manchester, Prestwick, Dublin, Paris, Amsterdam, Brussels.
'London VOLMET South'	128.6	Heathrow, Gatwick, Luton, Bournemouth, Stansted, East Midlands, Southend, Cardiff, Jersey.
'London VOLMET North'	126.6	Heathrow, Manchester, Glasgow, Edinburgh, Prestwick, Belfast, Aberdeen, Newcastle, Leeds

Order of information is: airport name, time, wind velocity, RVR, weather, cloud cover, temperature, dew point, QNH, tempo (forecast changes).

Significant Met (SIGMET)

When thunderstorms, line squalls, tropical revolving storms, heavy hail, severe turbulence, severe airframe icing, etc., has been reported, usually by pilots in flight, the information will be broadcast as a SIGMET.

Special Aerodrome Reports (SPEC)

Following changes of significance to an existing airfield weather report (e.g. sudden freezing rain, change in visibility, etc.) a special report will be transmitted by the ATS.

Privileges of the IMC Rating

The following table compares the minimum weather conditions as they apply to pilots holding an IMC Rating and those limited to a basic PPL.

Flight Condition	IMC Pilots	Non-IMC Pilots
Flying solo outside controlled airspace	No visibility limit	Min. visibility 1½ n.m.
Flying passengers outside controlled airspace	No visibility limit	Above 3000 ft. VMC. Below 3000 ft. 3 n.m.
Flying within Control Zones.	Special VFR when visibility at least 1½ n.m. or 1 n.m. while below cloud.	Special VFR when visibility at least 5 n.m.
Take-off/landing and other limits.	1 n.m.	All flights must remain in sight of the surface.

Period of Validity

The IMC Rating is valid for a period of 25 months, then a renewal test by an authorized examiner is required. It goes without saying that the rating page itself is no more than a sheet of paper. Its value depends upon keeping in practice because instrument flying is an exacting branch of aeronautics.

Chapter 10
Principles of Radio

Since it is unnecessary for the pilot to be a radio technician, the following explanations are deliberately couched in everyday terms with a view to providing a suitable background for the later chapters. The most non-technically minded is advised to read this chapter; for clearly the pilot with an elementary knowledge of radio principles is better able to derive full benefit from an aircraft's navigational and approach aids than his uninformed colleague.

Transmission and Reception

Radio waves are inaudible and invisible, their intangible nature making difficult both explanation and comprehension. For this reason it is convenient, certainly during the early stages, to think in terms of light rays, for these can not only be seen but their close relationship to radio waves makes the analogy both easy to understand and accurate.

A light fixed in a suitable prominent position may be seen by an observer from a number of miles away, the distance being dependent upon visibility, the strength of the source of light, the sensitivity of the eyesight of the observer, and because of the curvature of the earth's surface, height above the ground of the light and/or observer. This last factor should be remembered, because it has an important parallel in certain kinds of radio transmission. The light may take the form of a naked electric bulb (or even a bonfire), when it will be visible from all directions, or a reflector may be used to concentrate the light rays in a given direction, increasing the strength of the beam in that direction. Equipped with a shutter to interrupt the beam or a suitable electric switch, signals can be sent in morse code, the 'receiver' in this case being the eyes of the observer. Such a procedure was an established method of signalling long before the advent of radio, yet the two systems, radio waves and light rays, are in many ways remarkably similar.

It would be a simple matter to replace the eyes of the person receiving the light signals by a photo-electric cell, similar to the familiar light-meter built into many modern cameras. The minute electric currents from the photo-electric cell could be fed into an amplifier, which in turn worked a buzzer so that what started as a flashing light at the transmitting end finally becomes a signal in morse code audible to the receiver. Taking the principle a stage further, it would be possible to arrange the transmission of speech and music by employing a device capable of transforming sound vibrations into light flashes of varying intensities and indeed such an application forms the basis of recording sound on film.

While the method of transmission and reception is not the same in each case, many of the properties discussed so far are common to both light rays and radio waves. Radio waves may be **Beamed,** using suitable reflectors, and the shape of some of these has a marked resemblance to light reflectors of the familiar car headlamp type. Alternatively, radio waves may be so broadcast that the signals can be received from any direction. Transmitters of this type are called **Omni-directional** or **Non-directional.** In common with the signals lamp, the distance at which a radio wave may be received is dependent upon the power of the transmitter (power of the source of light) and the sensitivity of the radio receiver (the eyesight of the observer). Although radio is unaffected by visibility, many radio transmissions are blocked by the earth's curvature; mention has already been made of certain radio waves which behave like light rays in so far as the height above the ground of transmitter or receiver (or both) has a marked effect on the distance at which the signal can be received.

The question is often asked 'what is a radio wave?' and whereas the scientist can usually find a satisfactory answer to fundamental questions of this kind by enlisting mathematics, the practical pilot would in most cases find little to enlighten him in the scientist's notebook. Radio waves can, however, be described as **Electro-magnetic Energy,** propagated into space by a radio transmitter through its aerial. Although radio waves cannot be photographed or drawn, it is nevertheless possible to give a pictorial representation which is simple and worthy of being fully understood.

Figure 46 shows the radio wave as a fluctuating or **Alternating Current.** Starting from zero and increasing to its maximum strength it then declines and returns to zero when the sequence is repeated in the opposite polarity. The complete process as shown in the illustration is called a **Cycle** and the rate at which these cycles occur profoundly

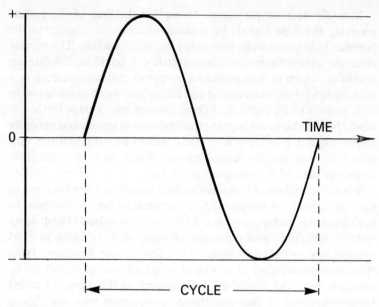

Fig. 46 The Radio (or Alternating Current) Cycle.

affects the behaviour and characteristics of the radio transmission and its reception.

Wavelength and Frequency

The term **Wavelength** has long found its place in everyday vocabulary, but it is usually associated with the selection of a favourite radio programme and the true meaning of the word is not always understood. By way of simple explanation, consider two horses galloping side by side at a speed of 40 ft/sec. Horse A takes four strides every second, covering 10 ft in each, whereas horse B has to gallop at five strides per second to maintain the same speed and therefore covers only 8 ft per stride. In other words the number of strides per second taken by a horse at a constant speed determines the length of each stride. Radio and light waves travel at the same speed and since by convention the metric system has been adopted in radio terminology, this speed is quoted as 300,000,000 metres per second (approximately seven times around the earth in one second). If the strides per second taken by the horse are replaced by cycles per second, it will be realized that the length of cycles will vary according to the frequency at which they occur. The length of each cycle in metres is the familiar wavelength and the number of cycles that occur per second is referred to as the **Frequency** (Fig. 47).

As far as the aircraft radio is concerned, it is customary to quote a station or facility as operating on a particular frequency, as opposed to the wavelength calibration, which finds common usage on most domestic radio receivers in Britain, although it will by now be realized that wavelength and frequency are merely different methods of specifying the same things.

Most household electricity supplies throughout the world are AC (alternating currents) generated at a frequency of 50 or 60 cycles per second, and this relatively slow fluctuation of current is often heard as 'mains hum' on mains-operated radio receivers and television sets.

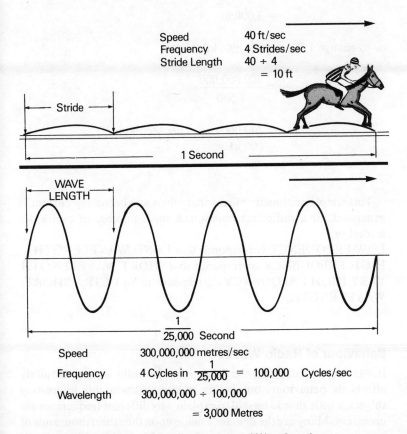

Speed	40 ft/sec
Frequency	4 Strides/sec
Stride Length	40 ÷ 4
	= 10 ft

Speed	300,000,000 metres/sec
Frequency	4 Cycles in $\frac{1}{25,000}$ = 100,000 Cycles/sec
Wavelength	300,000,000 ÷ 100,000
	= 3,000 Metres

Fig. 47   Relationship between Frequency and Wavelength.

Radio waves are generated at much higher frequencies and it is therefore more convenient to talk in terms of thousands of cycles or **kiloHertz** per second (kHz), in recognition of Heinrich Hertz (1857–1894) who discovered electro-magnetic waves. Very high frequencies are quoted in **MegaHertz** per second (MHz), i.e. millions of cycles per second or even **GigaHertz** (thousands of MegaHertz) per second. Conversion from wavelength to frequency, or frequency to wavelength, is a simple matter of dividing either measurement into 300,000,000 (speed in metres per second of electromagnetic waves), to obtain the other, e.g. to express 100 kHz in metres:

$$\text{wavelength} = \frac{300,000,000}{100,000}$$

$$= 3,000 \text{ m}$$

or to change 1,500 metres into kiloHertz:

$$\text{frequency} = \frac{300,000,000}{1,500}$$

$$= 200,000 \text{ cycles per second (c/s)}$$
$$= 200 \text{ kHz}$$

This simple arithmetic means that when an alternating current is generated for a radio transmission, a small number of cycles per second or:
LOW FREQUENCY corresponds to a LONG WAVELENGTH,
HIGH FREQUENCY corresponds to a SHORT WAVELENGTH
VERY HIGH FREQUENCY corresponds to an ULTRA SHORT WAVELENGTH.

Behaviour of Radio Waves

It was earlier stated that the frequency of a radio wave profoundly affects its behaviour, but before enlarging upon this interesting subject, a little should be said to explain why different frequencies are necessary. Many are the demands made upon the ether: thousands of broadcasting stations situated all over the world wish to make themselves heard. Then there are the long-distance telegraph services; communications between ship and shore, as well as aircraft and ground stations; television programmes and, more recently, radio links between satellites orbiting the earth in outer space and the launching authorities on the ground. It would not be possible to transmit all this on one frequency any more than it would be practicable to conduct thousands of telephone conversations simultaneously on one line. A less obvious objection to numerous radio stations operating on the same frequency is that when two transmissions are made at the same time, neither is readable, and a high-pitched whistle or **Heterodyne** results unless one of the transmitters is out of range of the receiver. In the interest of separation alone there is need for a wide range of frequencies and whereas the 200–2000 m **Waveband** (1500–150 kHz) was for many years capable of accommodating most of the 'domestic' radio stations operating throughout Europe, the problem of frequency space is now becoming acute. In any event, the performance of transmitters and receivers operating within these frequencies is unsuitable for aircraft communications and the various navigational and approach aids later to be described.

During the opening paragraphs of this chapter a comparison was made between light from a signals lamp and the energy radiated by a wireless transmitter. Possibly some readers may find the analogy too convenient to be convincing but it is nevertheless true, for although light rays occur at higher frequencies than radio waves, both are forms of electromagnetic energy. As the frequency is raised there comes a point when the electromagnetic energy enters a range of non-radio wavelengths. Infra-red rays occur followed by ordinary red light visible to the human eye. Progressive frequency increases cause the light to change colour through the visible spectrum. Ultra-violet and then x-rays follow at still higher frequencies. Infra-red rays are able to penetrate fog and cloud, while x-rays can reveal the inner structure of many solids. Both are invisible to the human eye, yet the essential difference between these extraordinary rays and the green light from a railwayman's lamp is merely one of frequency.

Lower down the scale, changes in frequency produce equally fundamental alterations in the behaviour of radio waves. The close relationship between light and radio waves is such that radio transmissions may be considered as low-frequency light signals, invisible to the eye and therefore requiring special equipment for detection in the form of a radio receiver of one kind or another (Fig. 48).

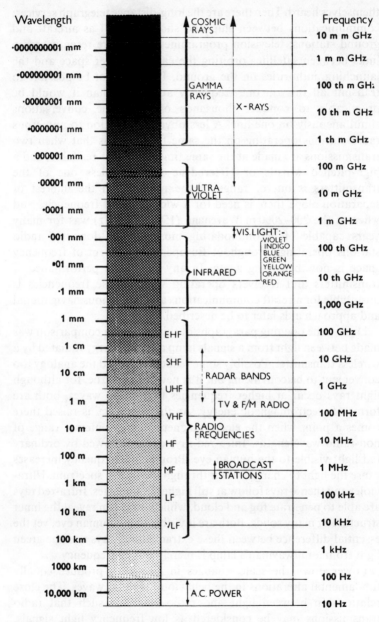

Fig. 48 The Electromagnetic Spectrum (10 m m GHz means ten million million GigaHertz and 100 th m GHz should be read as one hundred thousand million GigaHertz).

Frequency Bands

It has become the practice to classify radio transmissions into frequency bands or wavebands and these are summarized on page 174. Each band has its advantages and disadvantages. For example, the low, medium, and high frequencies (LF, MF, and HF) are all susceptible to interference from static, i.e. natural radiations caused by sunspots and thundery conditions. In extreme cases communications can be rendered practically unintelligible, particularly when heard against the noise of an aircraft's slipstream and engines. On the other hand, very high frequency (VHF) is remarkably free from static interference and, for reasons shortly to be explained, requires a less cumbersome aerial system than equipment operating on the lower frequencies. The disadvantage of VHF lies in its comparatively short range when used between one ground station and another, although when transmissions are made **Ground to Air,** i.e. from a ground station to an aircraft in flight, or air to ground, range improves with aircraft height, provided the equipment both in the air and on the ground is of sufficient power and sensitivity.

If the range of VHF is limited the reverse is true of HF (short wave), the next lower frequency band, for under favourable conditions clear reception is possible between Britain and America or even Australia. Why this should be is both interesting and important, as it affects the performance of certain radio navigational aids. Unless a transmitter is beamed so that radio is confined to a particular area, radio waves are propagated in all directions. Some travel parallel to the earth's surface and these **Ground Waves** may be detected by any radio

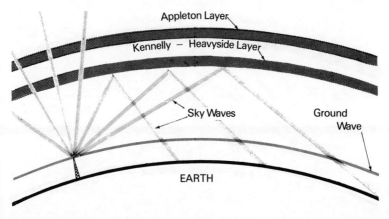

Fig. 49   Sky and Ground Waves.

receiver tuned to the frequency in use, provided of course that it is within range, for radio signals like light rays become fainter with distance. Other waves travel upwards at all angles to the horizontal and would disperse into outer space but for the layers of electrically charged or ionized gas which surround the earth. Named after their discoverers, the **Appleton** and **Kennelly-Heavyside layers** reflect back the signals to earth at an angle and intensity which varies according to frequency. It is these **Sky Waves** which make possible the transmission of radio signals over distances of many thousands of miles (Fig. 49).

The proportion of sky wave to ground wave also varies according to frequency. Very low frequency and low frequency transmissions depend almost entirely upon ground wave radiation. As the frequency is increased so the ground wave diminishes and the sky wave becomes predominant. At certain wavelengths it is possible to have an area that is outside the range of the ground wave, but too near the transmitter to detect the closest reflected or sky waves. Such an area is known as a **Skip Distance** and over that range no signals would be received, although reception may very likely be excellent at a greater distance from the transmitter (Fig. 50).

The ground wave ceases to exist from 20 MHz and above, reception being entirely dependent upon the sky wave, but from 45 mHz higher frequencies cause a fundamental change which accounts for the short range of VHF equipment. The sky wave is no longer reflected by the Kennelly-Heavyside layer but passes through the ionized gas and radiates into outer space. With no sky or ground

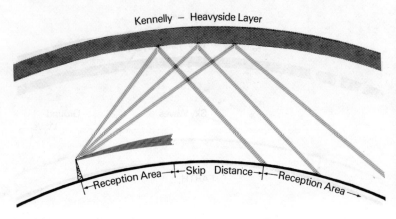

Fig. 50   No reception is possible within the Skip Distance area.

wave VHF radio takes on the characteristics of a beam of light and if contact is to be maintained, the receiver must have an uninterrupted view of the sender, and hills, tall buildings, or the earth's curvature all limit the range of VHF transmissions. (Such effects are common experience with Television Channels and the various 'F/M' sound programmes which are also in the VHF band.) In other words, the range of a VHF transmitter, however powerful it may be, is limited to **Line of Sight,** and while the term is self-explanatory, Fig. 51 will make clear the effect of the earth's curvature and show how the range between a VHF ground station and an aircraft in flight is dependent upon the altitude of the aircraft.

It is now opportune to summarize the radio frequency bands, their uses, advantages, and disadvantages (see page 174).

The Transmitter

Radio communication is dependent upon radio waves which, as already explained, are high frequency alternating currents and, like other kinds of electric currents, they must be generated. Household and industrial electricity is generated by a mechanical device called an alternator, and whilst this method is ideal for the low frequency mains supply alternating at 50 or 60 Hz, other means have to be found for radio frequencies where the number of cycles per second in common use ranges between 3000 and 30,000,000,000 (3 kHz to

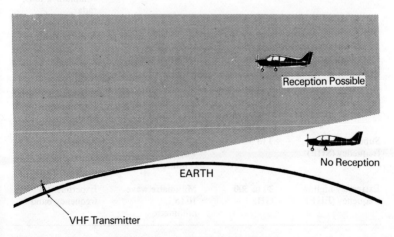

Fig. 51 'Line-of-sight' limitation of VHF transmission.

Radio Frequency Band	Frequency Limits	Equivalent Wavelength	Remarks
Very low frequency (VLF)	3 to 30 kHz	Very long wave (VLW) 100,000 to 10,000 metres	Long-range communication service, Omega and other VLF area navigation systems
Low frequency (LF)	30 to 300 kHz	Long wave (LW) 10,000 to 1000 metres	Broadcast programmes, long-range communications, and navigational aids
Medium frequency (MF)	300 kHz to 3 MHz	Medium wave (MW) 1000 to 100 metres	Broadcast programmes, short-range communications and navigational aids
High frequency (HF)	3 to 30 MHz	Short wave (SW) 100 to 10 metres	Broadcast programmes, and long-distance communications
Very high frequency (VHF)	30 to 300 MHz	Metre wave 10 to 1 metre	Television programmes, short-range communications, radar, navigational, and approach aids
Ultra high frequency (UHF)	300 to 3000 MHz	Decimetre wave 10 to 1 decimetre	Television programmes and short-range communications for military aircraft
Super high frequency (SHF)	3 to 30 GHz	Centimetre wave 10 to 1 centimetre	Radar
Extremely high frequency (EHF)	30 to 300 GHz	Millimetre wave 10 to 1 millimetre	Experimental frequency band

30,000 MHz). Because it is outside the capabilities of rotating mechanical parts to function at such speeds, the AC generator or alternator as used in the power station is replaced in a radio transmitter by an electronic circuit called an **Oscillator,** a relatively simple arrangement of coils, condensers, and valves, or transistors which is adjusted to alternate at whatever transmitting frequency is required. The oscillator produces a radio signal, too weak for practical transmission, so that an **Amplifier,** similar in some respects to the type used for public address systems, is incorporated in the transmitter to increase the power of the radio signal before it is led to the aerial.

The transmitting aerial is an important factor in satisfactory radio communications, and for the best results it should approximate in length to the wavelength in use. The significance of this will be explained in the section dealing with the receiver on page 176. Ideally a transmitter working on a wavelength of 1000 m (300 kHz) requires an aerial 1000 m in length, and although **Halfwave** aerials can be successful, even 500 m of wire is longer than the biggest ocean liner and certainly cannot be fixed in a permanent position on any aeroplane. Frequencies requiring long aerials have gone out of favour for aircraft use, but before the advent of more modern equipment the difficulty was overcome by having a **Trailing Aerial** that could be winched in and out of the aircraft as required.

Herein lies one of the disadvantages of long wavelengths for aircraft radio. Nevertheless, for the purpose of this explanation 1000 m is a convenient figure and it can be assumed that an oscillator

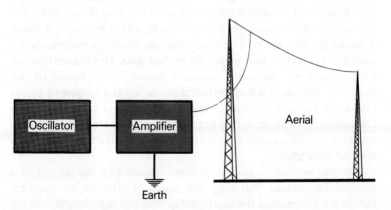

Fig. 52   Simple transmitter.

175

has been tuned to generate an alternating current with a wavelength of 1000 m, i.e. a frequency of 300 kHz. This weak signal is fed into an amplifier and the two wires carrying the now highly magnified signal are connected, one to the aerial and one to earth (Fig. 52). The simple transmitter begins to radiate electromagnetic energy into the ether at a frequency of 300 kHz.

The nature of this radiation may be demonstrated by throwing a stone into a calm lake. The surface is disturbed by rings which spread in ever-increasing numbers and create the impression that water is flowing outwards from the stone's point of entry. In fact there is no movement from the centre and twigs or leaves floating on the surface of the lake remain where they are, merely undulating up and down as each ripple develops, transmitting energy to the water and forming yet another concentric ring.

The Receiver

Imagine a radio receiver situated some distance away from the transmitter described in the preceding paragraphs. Its aerial, or for that matter any aerial, is assailed by countless signals, minute electromagnetic waves emanating from broadcast stations, ships at sea, and aircraft in flight. Yet notwithstanding this galaxy of radio transmissions, the receiver is able to select and reproduce the 1000 m signal from the transmitter already described to the exclusion of all others. The seemingly impossible is accomplished by utilizing the principle of **Resonance,** a phenomenon popularly associated with the ability of certain opera singers to shatter a wine glass by singing the correct note. Resonance may be demonstrated quite convincingly with a piano. Having first depressed the sustaining (loud) pedal, the instrument can be made to 'play' any note within its range, without depressing a key, merely by singing the note required, preferably in a loud voice and close to the open lid of the piano. This occurs because each string has a particular vibration period. To quote one or two examples, middle C is usually tuned to vibrate at a frequency of 261 c/s, while top and bottom C have a frequency of 2088 and 33 c/s respectively. Any note with a pitch of 261 c/s will resonate middle C on the piano, i.e. cause it to vibrate in sympathy like the opera singer and the wine glass.

Wireless aerials do not, of course, vibrate like the strings of a musical instrument, but they are similarly affected by electrical resonance and indeed the relationship between wavelength and the length of a transmitting aerial has already been mentioned. Whereas the piano string can be made to vibrate at the correct sound frequency, a transmitting or receiving aerial becomes electrically active at the correct radio frequency. In effect, when the tuning dial of a radio receiver is rotated in search of a particular signal the resonance of its aerial circuit is altered to match the frequency of the transmitting station. It only remains to amplify the minute signal received by the aerial so that it can be fed to a loudspeaker or headset (Fig. 53).

Audio Frequencies

The 1000 m signal radiated by the simple transmitter described on page 173 is called a **Carrier Wave** and it produces nothing more in a radio receiver than a toneless hiss, the sound often heard on an ordinary radio set during brief periods when neither speech nor music is in progress. This carrier wave may be likened to the steady beam of light from the signals lamp mentioned early in the chapter, and as such it must be modified in much the same way as the light signal if it is to be of any use as a means of communication. Like the signals lamp the simplest method is to interrupt the carrier wave so that a coded signal is produced such as morse code. Usually originating from ships at sea, an ordinary domestic receiver tuned to the shipping band (80–200 m) will often pick up these morse signals as a series of toneless dots and dashes. Radio receivers on board ship may be switched to add their own tone to the carrier wave when required, and

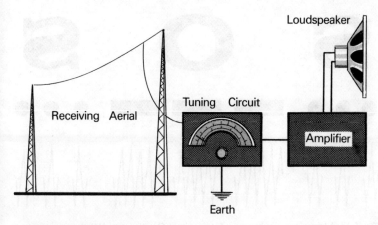

Fig. 53 Simple receiver.

although morse signals are now rarely used on aircraft, the interrupted carrier wave represents the simplest method of radio communication and is illustrated in Fig. 54.

For the transmission of speech, sounds of a recognizable pitch, and music, additional circuits and electronic components are required at the transmitting and receiving end, but before these are described, a little should be understood about the type of sound which can be detected by the human ear.

Sound is caused by vibrating any medium at audible frequencies and is transmitted by the surrounding air, the pitch of the note varying according to the frequency of the vibration. Although sound frequencies are often quoted in cycles per second, they bear no similarity to radio frequencies, and the two should not be confused. Sound waves are purely mechanical, air vibrations which impinge upon the ear drum and register in the brain of the listening animal. Sound can also travel through solids and fluids, but it is entirely dependent upon such a physical medium for its existence. Indeed sound cannot travel in a vacuum, whereas radio waves can do so and are transmitted through the airless regions of outer space.

Certain animals are able to hear notes which are inaudible to the human ear, and while hearing, like eyesight, varies from one person to another, generally the range of **Audio Frequencies,** as they are called, lies between 30 c/s at the lowest and 30,000 c/s at the top end of the musical scale.

Speech is made up of a complex combination of tones, varying in

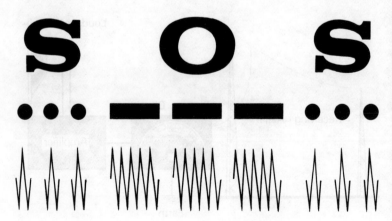

Fig. 54 Morse transmitted by Interrupted Continuous Wave.

pitch and quality and for the purpose of transmission these are collected by a microphone which translates the resultant air vibrations into minute electrical currents. It now remains to 'print' these audio frequencies upon the carrier wave for onward transmission, and the circuit or **Stage** of the transmitter responsible for this function is called a **Modulator.** It accomplishes its task in one of two ways:

1. **Amplitude Modulation** (A/M) where the strength of the carrier wave is varied in step with the sound wave, or
2. **Frequency Modulation** (F/M) where the frequency of the carrier wave is varied in step with the sound wave. This method is in use for most domestic programmes broadcast on VHF.

Both methods of modulation are illustrated in Fig. 55.

At the receiver the modulated carrier wave is first amplified before passing to the **Detector** stage. Here the audio frequencies are collected while the unwanted radio frequencies of the carrier wave are removed. The audio frequencies may be amplified to whatever level is required and then fed to either headphones or a loudspeaker so that the electric currents undulating at audio frequency can be made to vibrate a diaphragm, which in turn produces air vibrations audible to the human ear. The complete sequence, expressed stage by stage, is explained in Figs. 56 and 57.

Radar

Transmission and reception, as it has so far been explained, involves the radiation of a modulated or unmodulated continuous or interrupted continuous wave and as such it is classified as Radio. Under the stimulus of a war a need arose for the speedy location of enemy aircraft by ground stations controlling the defending fighters. There was also a requirement for airborne equipment which could be used by night fighters in their search for bombers operating under cover of darkness. An 'intermittent' form of radio was developed for the purpose and from it came a number of variations, some of which have been adapted to more peaceful use. All variants, civil and military, are called **Pulse Systems.**

It has already been explained that the Kennelly-Heavyside layer reflects certain radio waves. Indeed this layer, and the still higher **Appleton Layer,** make possible the transmission of radio over long distances. Early experiments showed that when a VHF or UHF (Ultra High Frequency) beam was transmitted in pulse form solid or

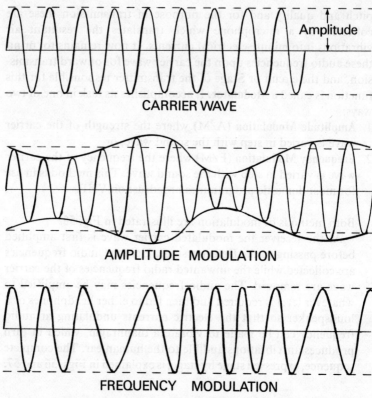

Amplitude

CARRIER WAVE

AMPLITUDE MODULATION

FREQUENCY MODULATION

Fig. 55   Modulation is the method used to 'print' speech or music on the carrier wave. It is achieved by Amplitude Modulation (centre drawing) or Frequency Modulation (bottom drawing).

semi-solid objects reflected back each pulse. The much weaker reflected pulse could be received at the transmitting end and the interval between transmission and reception was timed electronically so that the distance between the object and the transmitter could be determined. The 'echo' could be displayed on a cathode ray tube, suitably marked with a **Time Base** scale along which the echo would appear according to its distance from the transmitter. Within limits, and with certain refinements, such a cathode ray tube will indicate whether the object is directly ahead of the beam or if it lies to the left or right.

Figure 58 shows the **Display** with this type of equipment – when a pulse is reflected back it appears on the cathode ray screen as a **Blip**, the common name for an echo of this kind. In this relatively simple form pulse systems are used for certain navigational aids, but these are of a type unlikely to interest readers of this book. Nevertheless the time base scale as illustrated in Fig. 58 forms the basis of an important aid to be described on pages 226–232. At this stage it is sufficient to say that when the original transmission is reflected back to the sender and then displayed on a cathode ray screen such a pulse system no longer comes under the heading of 'radio' but is classified as **Primary Radar,** the word 'radar' being derived from Radio Detection And Ranging.

It has already been explained that suitable beamed VHF or UHF pulses are reflected by objects of a solid or semi-solid nature. By this it is meant that in addition to receiving an echo from aircraft, high ground, etc., radar will reflect and produce a cathode ray blip when it encounters certain types of cloud or even heavy rain. Whereas this property has made possible the use of airborne weather radar capable of warning flight crews of thunder clouds ahead, there are times when this extreme sensitivity becomes a disadvantage, a typical example being the obliteration of an aircraft's echo on a ground controller's screen occasioned by the presence of heavy rain. This is a problem which can partly be solved by choosing a waveband less prone to cloud or rain reflexion, but a more complete answer makes use of additional airborne equipment called a **Transponder,** which like radar itself owes its development to the Second World War.

Summary

The foregoing explanations are intended to provide the pilot with a working knowledge of radio and radar. While in the interest of simplicity this section has been limited to essentials it should nevertheless enable the reader to understand the various navigational and approach aids mentioned in this book. Meanwhile the preceding pages can be summarized in the following few sentences.

Radio waves may be considered as low-frequency light rays and the behaviour of radio and light is in many respects remarkably similar. Signals are generated by an OSCILLATOR as high-frequency ALTERNATING CURRENTS, amplified, and then led to an aerial which must be proportional in length to the wavelength of the signal. Such an aerial will RESONATE and emit ELECTROMAGNETIC ENERGY in the form of radio waves, which propagate at a speed of 300 million metres per second. The transmission is called a CARRIER WAVE and it is quoted as being of a particular frequency

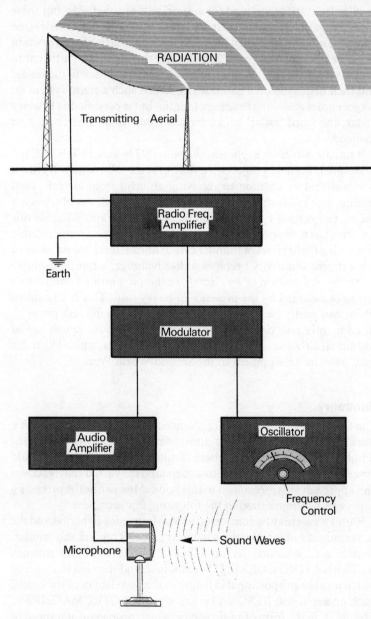

Fig. 56 From sound waves to radiation (transmission).

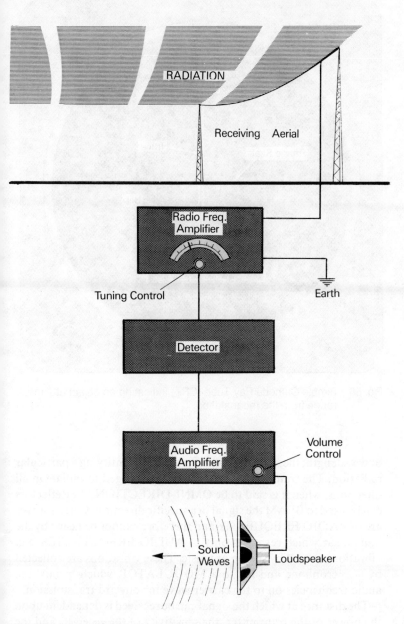

Fig. 57   From radiation to sound waves (reception).

183

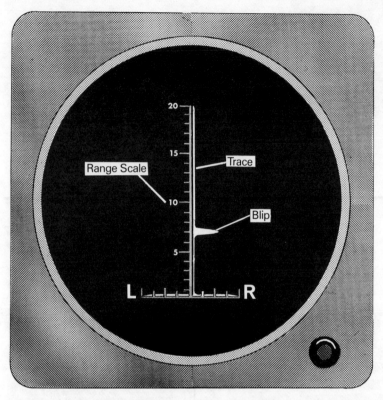

Fig. 58 Simple Cathode Ray Tube (CRT) indicating an object at 7 miles range from the radar station.

or wavelength; these are different methods of identifying a particular radiation. The transmitting aerial may be arranged to radiate in all directions, when it is said to be OMNI-DIRECTIONAL. Reflectors can be used to BEAM the signal in a specific direction. Carrier waves are of RADIO FREQUENCY and therefore cannot be heard by the human ear which responds only to AUDIO FREQUENCIES, e.g. vibrations caused by speech or music. These vibrations are collected by a microphone and led to a MODULATOR which 'prints' the audio frequencies on to the carrier wave for onward transmission.

The distance at which the signal can be received is dependent upon the power of the transmitter, the sensitivity of the receiver, and the frequency of the carrier wave. Low-frequency transmitters radiate a GROUND WAVE which follows the earth's curvature, while a SKY

WAVE may be reflected by the KENNELLY-HEAVISIDE and APPLETON LAYERS. Higher frequencies are more dependent upon the sky than the ground wave, which disappears at still higher frequencies. VHF passes through the two layers, has no ground wave, and like a light signal is dependent for contact between transmitter and receiver on LINE OF SIGHT.

The receiver has a RADIO FREQUENCY AMPLIFIER which incorporates a tuning circuit. This alters the resonance of the receiving aerial circuit to match the desired wavelength. The output from the RF amplifier is fed to a DETECTOR STAGE which removes the unwanted carrier wave and passes on the audio frequencies to the final amplification stage. This in turn is connected to a headset or loudspeaker. In each case electrical energy of audio frequency is made to vibrate a diaphragm and so produce a replica of the original sound entering the transmitting microphone.

RADAR is a development of radio. PULSE SYSTEMS beam VHF or UHF transmission in a particular direction. When a pulse encounters an aircraft or other solid object, part of it is reflected back to the sending source and causes an echo or BLIP to appear on the screen of a CATHODE RAY TUBE. An electronic timing device measures the range of the object, which is indicated by the position of the blip in relation to a TIME BASE SCALE. This particular type of pulse system is called PRIMARY RADAR. Under conditions of heavy rain, echoes are sometimes reproduced on the cathode ray screen which obliterates the blip from an aircraft unless it is equipped with a TRANSPONDER. This small airborne transmitter is triggered by a searching radar pulse and the signal it returns produces a powerful blip, readily distinguishable on a cathode ray screen affected by rain echoes. Such a system is known as SECONDARY RADAR.

Chapter 11
The Radio Aids

Chapters 4 to 8 cover the use of radio aids in the course of instrument flight. This chapter explains, in simple terms, the working principles and operation of the equipment.

The reliability of radio equipment has greatly improved since the introduction of **Solid State** technology which, in the main, eliminates soldered joints and moving parts. But aircraft radio must be treated with care and consideration if it is to provide good service.

While some light trainers may be confined to a single communications set and a NAV receiver for the VOR, for instrument flight this and other radio equipment is duplicated as an insurance against radio failure. Duplicated equipment also offers a number of other advantages during radio navigation, particularly when a simultaneous fix is required from two stations.

On no account should radio equipment be switched on while engine starting is in progress because serious damage may be caused following a current surge. To allow quick isolation or activation of the radio installation, without having to switch on or off eight or more separate pieces of equipment, it is the practice in some aircraft to fit an **Avionics Master Switch.**

Communications

The Transmitter/Receiver (Transceiver) is the link between pilot and the various ATC services. In most light/general aviation aircraft it operates in the VHF band. Transport aircraft requiring worldwide communications also carry HF equipment and for military purposes UHF is used. Transceivers may be separate units or they can be combined within the same case as the NAV receiver (used for VOR and ILS reception). Methods of operation are similar in each case.

In larger aircraft, where instrument panel space is at a premium, the radio equipment is usually stacked in a radio bay located some distance from the flight deck. The control heads and their indicators are conveniently positioned on the instrument panel or central console. Such an arrangement is known as **Indirect Switching**. In light and the smaller general aviation aircraft it is usual to install radio equipment in the instrument panel complete with its controls and readouts. This is known as **Direct Switching** and it is the arrangement most likely to be encountered by pilots studying for an IMC Rating.

Operation

There has been a progressive move towards simplicity of operation and uniformity of control layout. The following description will explain the working procedures likely to be encountered.

When the transceiver is switched on (in some cases by a separate switch, in others by the initial rotation of the volume control) the receiver is operative and the transmitter is on 'stand-by'. Whatever signals are received may be reproduced either through the pilot's headset or via a cabin loudspeaker. Provision is usually made for more than one headset and the cabin speaker may be muted if required. When reception is through the cabin loudspeaker a hand microphone incorporating a 'press to transmit' button is provided. This type of microphone may also be used when a headset is worn but, more usually, the headset will be fitted with a **Boom Microphone** and the transmit button will be located on the control column or wheel. In either case the action of pressing the button cuts out the receiver and brings into circuit the transmitter.

Selecting Frequencies

It was previously explained that separation of one station from another is achieved by tuning both transmitter and receiver. In each case the resonance of the aerial circuit is altered until the correct frequency is reached (p. 176). Most domestic receivers may be tuned progressively from one end of their tuning scale to the other. Within the frequency range of the set any frequency may be obtained by turning the tuning knob, which in turn alters a variable condenser. This is called **Continuous Tuning**, a method adequate for locating broadcasting stations in the LF and MF bands (long and medium wavelengths). Its disadvantage lies in the fact that as the frequency increases so the degree of adjustment becomes finer; any home radio capable of receiving short-wave stations will illustrate the point. VHF tuning is in turn more critical than HF so that continuous tuning is unsuitable for the purpose, particularly when the pilot is required to change frequencies a number of times within a short period. In relatively inexpensive transceivers (not intended for aircraft use) the problem is eased by spreading a small frequency range over a large tuning scale.

The advent of 720-channel transceivers with 25 kHz spacing was made possible by the development of a frequency control method known as a synthesizer but there is no need for pilots to have a detailed knowledge of these. Frequency selection is made with two rotary knobs, one for MHz and the other for kHz in steps of 25.

Other controls are limited to a volume control for the receiver, an 'on/off' switch when this is not incorporated in the volume control, and a background noise limiter called a **Squelch** control, which should be turned down until interference becomes negligible. The squelch control must be used with discretion, since by attempting to eliminate background noise completely the sensitivity of the receiver may be reduced to the point where messages from weak stations go unheard. In some modern equipment squelch is fully automatic. A typical 720-channel transceiver is illustrated in Fig. 59.

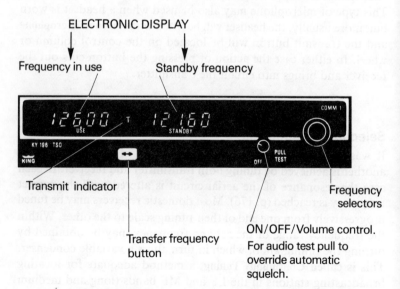

Fig. 59   King KY 196 communications transceiver with electronic frequency display and the ability to store a second frequency for instant use.

Frequency Storage

Since the first VHF transceivers were introduced for RAF service during the Second World War there have been a number of changes in methods of frequency selection. The first equipment was limited to four frequencies selected by push buttons and later transceivers offered eight channels. Then came ten channel sets with rotary selectors.

The most common arrangement for civil equipment is the one already described where two knobs are used to select the frequencies, one for MHz and the other controlling fractions of a MHz in steps of 25 kHz. Usually the readout takes the form of numbers similar to those in a car mileage indicator but there are now many sets which have an electronic display (Fig. 59). A further development is one that eliminates all mechanical switching, the usual source of failure in electronic equipment, replacing it with a push button keyboard similar to that of a pocket calculator. The frequency required is selected on the buttons, a readout is verified and, if correct, brought into use by pressing the USE button. This type of equipment usually forms part of a complete system embracing communications and navigational equipment.

A feature of this advanced equipment which is shared by some transceivers without press button selection is the ability to store two or more frequencies in a manner similar to the memory facility of most pocket calculators. The frequencies are entered into the equipment when they are available for instant recall by using the appropriate switch or button provided.

The Use of RTF

The practical handling of R/T sets needs little explanation. Frequency selection was outlined earlier in the chapter, most modern equipment being instantly tuned. The range to be expected from low-powered VHF sets may be regarded as approximately 10 n.m. for every 1000 ft above the ground and twice that figure with more powerful equipment operating under good conditions. These points should be remembered:

1. When switching on or changing frequency avoid interrupting other R/T which may be in progress by listening for a few moments before transmitting.
2. Speak clearly and deliberately near the microphone. Shouting will usually distort transmission and is to be avoided.

3. Although it is not usually necessary when using the Q-code, the phonetic alphabet (Appendix III) must be utilized whenever there is risk of being misunderstood, e.g. when transmitting aircraft call signs.

VHF Direction Finding (VDF)

The use of radio signals for the purpose of direction finding is practically as old as radio itself and D/F is probably the earliest of the radio aids. The directional properties of certain types of radio aerial are well known and may be demonstrated by rotating the case of a portable radio until the signal fades to a low level, or even completely. By attaching a compass scale to the radio case and rotating it against a fixed line running North/South the bearing may be assessed of any broadcasting station. The portable radio has now become a simple D/F set.

Early direction finding equipment embodied a **Loop Aerial** (Fig. 60), which could be rotated in a manner similar to the portable radio. At the point of minimum signal strength, called a **Null,** a bearing was read off the scale attached to the loop.

The information was transmitted back to the calling aircraft in one of the following forms:

QDR: magnetic bearing of aircraft in relation to D/F station.

QTE: true bearing of aircraft in relation to D/F station.

QDM: magnetic heading to be steered by aircraft to reach the D/F station in conditions of zero wind.

In more recent years it has become the practice to confine bearing information to QDM or QTE.

The loop aerial senses direction according to the relative signal strength received in its vertical portions (shaded sections in Fig. 60). When the loop is presented edge on to a transmitter the current received by the vertical portion nearest the transmitter will flow to the D/F receiver. This is the position of maximum signal strength. By rotating the loop until its plane faces the transmitter (i.e. both vertical sections face the transmitter) a balance in current will occur and no signal will flow to the D/F receiver, thus causing a Null (Fig. 61).

As there are two maximum signal positions (either vertical section

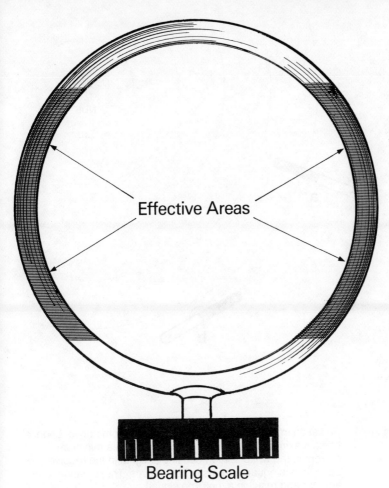

Effective Areas

Bearing Scale

Fig. 60   Simple Loop Aerial showing directionally
sensitive vertical areas.

pointing towards the transmitter) and two nulls (either face of the
loop towards the transmitter), provision must be made to ensure that
reciprocal bearings are not sent to the calling aircraft. This is achieved
by comparing the signals received on the loop with a fixed non-
directional aerial switched in for the purpose; a procedure called
Sensing.

The older type of equipment so far described worked in the MF and
HF bands. W/T (**Wireless Telegraphy** in Morse Code) was used by the

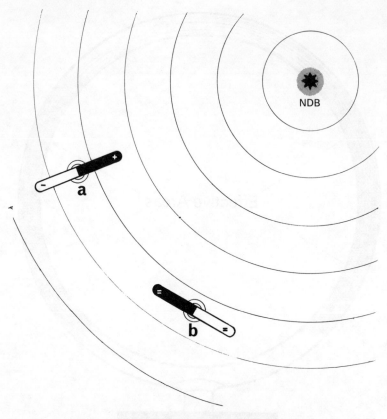

Fig. 61   Radiation from the transmitter (NDB) seen from above. Loop 'a' has a maximum current in the black half and a minimum current in the white portion causing a signal in the receiver. Loop 'b' has equal currents in both halves. These cancel one another and result in a 'null' (no signal).

aircraft calling for D/F assistance and the station passing the bearing information. Particularly on HF and the higher medium frequencies the accuracy of bearings taken after hours of daylight deteriorated because of **Night Effect**. After dark the Kennelly-Heaviside and Appleton layers (p. 172) ascend from their daytime height of approximately 30 miles to 200 or so miles above the earth, altering the angle of the reflected sky waves which now approach the loop aerial from above, avoiding the vertical sections which are essential for direction finding purposes (Fig. 62).

The virtual disappearance of MF and HF morse code for aircraft

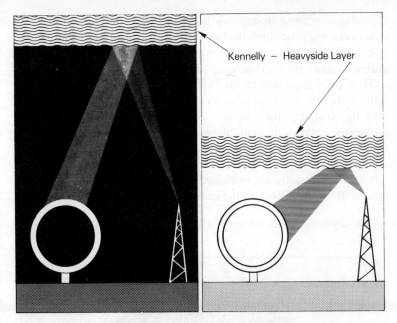

Kennelly — Heavyside Layer

Fig. 62   Night Effect. D/F inaccuracies occur at night when the
Kennelly-Heavyside Layer ascends and sky waves meet the
loop aerial from above. Compare with daytime picture on the
right.

communications purposes, and its replacement by VHF Radio
Telephony, has likewise brought about the elimination of MF and
most HF direction finding services, the function now being
performed by VHF D/F or, as it is commonly known, VDF. Based
upon the use of radio telephony, VDF is free of night effect, because
there is no sky wave, radio contact being dependent upon direct 'line
of sight' as is always the case with VHF transmission and reception
(p. 173).

Cathode Ray D/F

Whereas the older VDF ground stations employ a manually operated
direction finding aerial, requiring a prolonged transmission from the
calling aircraft in order to determine a null and obtain a reading,
airfields offering D/F service now use an improved form of
VDF called **Cathode Ray D/F**. With this equipment a reading is

193

instantaneous and automatic, without the need for a long transmission or sensing procedure, the bearing being displayed as a thin radial trace on a cathode ray tube. There is no danger of ambiguity and a spring loaded switch on the equipment enables the operator to obtain a QDM or, if requested by the calling aircraft, a QTE (Fig. 63). The immediate indication provided by the equipment eliminates the time-wasting 'transmit for bearing' procedure associated with older moveable aerial equipment, allowing bearings to be passed at more frequent intervals. It is usual to link the cathode ray direction-finding equipment to the 'approach' frequency so that all air-to-ground communications are accompanied by a bearing which is ready for immediate transmission to the calling aircraft if required.

Fig. 63   Cathode ray direction finding. Set illustrated is showing a QDM of 155.

Accuracy

At some airfields the use of VDF is limited to the secondary role of assisting operators to identify aircraft on radar screens. When in addition a D/F service is available, this will be promulgated in the various radio navigation flight guides as providing a VDF service. Operators of VDF stations have authority to refuse bearings to a pilot when conditions are such that the accuracy of the QDM or QTE is in doubt. In this event the reason will be passed to the pilot at the time of refusal. Bearings are classed in three categories of accuracy as follows:

Class A accurate within ± 2°
Class B accurate within ± 5°
Class C accurate within ± 10°

In common with all VHF communications, the range at which VDF can be used is limited by considerations of 'line of sight'.

Associated Airborne Equipment

Irrespective of the type of equipment at the D/F station, the only requirement in the aircraft is a VHF transceiver.

Use of VDF

Because there is in existence a complete system of navigational aids and in order to avoid congestion of the communication frequencies, VDF must not be used for *en route* navigational purposes unless there has been a failure of the radio navigational equipment in the aircraft or on the ground. As already explained, VDF is used at some airports as a means of identification by radar operators. Other than for emergency navigational purposes, VDF finds its main application in **Let-down Procedures.** As the term implies, let-down procedures are a means of assisting an aircraft to descend in safety when the ground is obscured by low cloud or poor visibility. There are various let-down procedures utilizing different equipment; the **VDF Let-down Procedure** is dealt with in Chapter 4.

VHF Omni-directional Radio Range & Distance Measuring Equipment (VOR/DME)

VOR is a VHF aid operating within the 108–118 MHz frequency band. Ground equipment is confined to a small compact transmitter called a **VOR** which may be located on or near an airfield or within an airway to provide *en route* guidance. Its principle of operation is as follows.

On pages 165–168 alternating current cycles and the direct relationship between an alternating current and a radio wave were explained in general terms. Referring again to Fig. 46 on page 166, it will be seen that during transmission an alternating current or radio wave increases its potential from zero to maximum positive, declines through zero, and continues to maximum negative, returning again to zero for the commencement of another cycle.

The state of the current or radio wave at any given time, called its **Phase,** may be measured on a suitable meter. When two simultaneous transmissions of differing phase are radiated over an area, an instrument designed to measure changes in phase relationship between the transmitters may be adapted to indicate the position of an aircraft. Such a radio navigational system is dependent for its function upon **Phase Comparison** and VOR is an example of a Phase Comparison aid.

Radiating in all directions, the VOR station transmits two patterns, one fixed or **Reference Phase Signal** of constant phase and a second **Variable Phase Signal** which alters phase as it rotates, so that aircraft flying around the station receive two signals of constantly altering phase relationship. In effect the VOR transmits an infinite number of radials each of slightly differing character, so that readings on a phase comparison meter would vary according to its bearing in relation to the beacon. A three-letter identification signal is transmitted in morse at 10-sec. intervals by the VOR, which will have a range of 50–200 n.m., according to the power of the transmitter and the height of the aircraft. (Because it is a VHF aid, ground to air range is dependent upon the usual 'line-of-sight' consideration.)

Associated Airborne Equipment

The aircraft installation comprises:

1. A NAV receiver capable of receiving navigational frequencies in the VHF band.

2. An **Omni-bearing Indicator.**

1. Navigation Receiver

VOR stations are received on the Navigation receiver which may either be a separate unit or incorporated within the same case as the communications transceiver. Such an installation is called a NAV/COM set and it is usually only found in smaller aircraft. A typical example (illustrated in Fig. 64) includes a 720-channel transmitter/receiver for communications purposes and a separate 200-channel NAV receiver, which may be tuned to a VOR or ILS (pages 217–26) without interrupting the communications transceiver. The NAV receiver has a separate volume control, allowing VOR and ILS signals to be identified and then reduced to a level allowing R/T to be conducted without distraction. COM and NAV facilities in some equipment are switched on together by the same control (either a separate ON-OFF switch or one that is incorporated

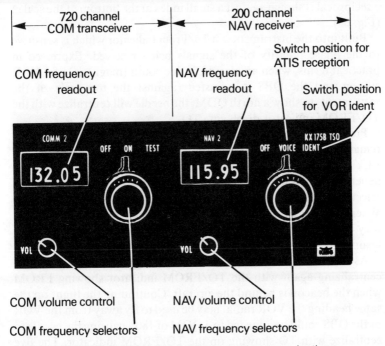

Fig. 64   King KX 175B combined 720 channel communications transceiver and 200 channel navigation receiver.

with the volume control for the COM transceiver), while other installations have separate switching. However, the controls are clearly marked and easy to understand.

2. Omni-bearing Indicator

The Omni-bearing Indicator incorporates an adjustable phase meter which converts VOR signals (amplified by the NAV receiver) into visual indications by comparing the difference in phase between the two signals radiated by the VOR. A vertical needle in the instruments 'instructs' the pilot to 'FLY LEFT' or 'FLY RIGHT' according to the position of the aircraft in relation to the VOR and the setting of the adjustable meter which is altered on the **Omni-bearing Selector (OBS)**. The needle may be centralized by rotating the OBS knob; this re-aligns the instrument to conform with the signal phases being received at the time. Geared to the omni-bearing selector is a rotating scale which translates the phase comparison function of the instrument into magnetic bearings in relation to the VOR being received. A QDM is read off the scale at the top of the instrument and a reciprocal is shown against a small index at the bottom of the scale* (Fig. 65).

Built into the instrument is a **To/From Indicator** which is sensitive to the phase polarity of the signals being received. Expressed in practical terms, when an aircraft is due south (magnetic) of a VOR station and the OBS is adjusted (against the top scale of the instrument) to show a north QDM, the needle will centralize with the TO/FROM indicator displaying TO.

Provided the aircraft flies on the selected QDM the needle will remain in the centre, a drift to the left causing it to instruct the pilot to FLY RIGHT and vice versa, the amount of needle deflection being dependent upon the degree of aircraft displacement away from the selected radial, each dot on the scale representing approximately 2½°. When drift has caused the needle to move left or right a new QDM may be determined by adjusting the OBS until the needle centres again.

As the VOR is overflown the needle will fluctuate from side to side, centralizing again with the TO/FROM indicator showing FROM when the beacon is behind the aircraft. Continuing the flight on the same heading the VOR radial may be used to fly away from the VOR or the OBS could be adjusted to a QDM of 180°, causing the needle to centralize with TO showing on the TO/FROM indicator. The five

---

*Some instruments have the scales reversed.

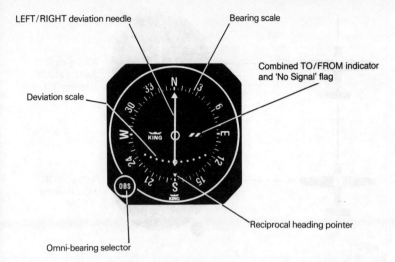

LEFT/RIGHT deviation needle

Bearing scale

Combined TO/FROM indicator and 'No Signal' flag

Deviation scale

Reciprocal heading pointer

Omni-bearing selector

Fig. 65   Typical VOR indicator. This type has a combined TO/FROM indicator and 'NO SIGNAL' flag.

stages just described are illustrated in Fig. 66. However, it should be understood that the needle will only provide 'Fly Left/Fly Right' commands in the correct sense provided the OBS is adjusted so that the instrument reads TO while flying towards, and FROM when flying away from the VOR.

The clear indication provided by the equipment when the aircraft is over the transmitter enables VORs to be used as Reporting Points. As compared with other radio aids VOR is possessed of these advantages:

1. Transmitting on VHF it is free from static interference.
2. Simple to tune and operate.
3. Little risk of ambiguity.
4. It may be incorporated with ILS (a radio landing aid described later in the chapter), saving weight and valuable space on the instrument panel.
5. The Omni-bearing Indicator identifies VOR radials irrespective of the aircraft's heading, which is therefore ignored when determining a QDM or its reciprocal (Fig. 67).

Use and Limitations

VOR will only provide a position when an 'over the beacon' signal is received. It is standard practice to install two VOR sets in an aircraft

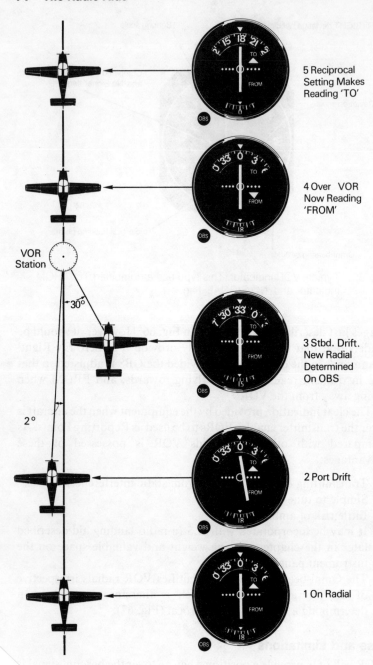

5 Reciprocal Setting Makes Reading 'TO'

4 Over VOR Now Reading 'FROM'

VOR Station

30°

3 Stbd. Drift. New Radial Determined On OBS

2°

2 Port Drift

1 On Radial

66 Homing to a VOR station.

equipped for instrument flying, such an arrangement providing a simultaneous fix using suitably located VORs. The value of a single VOR installation is considerably enhanced when it is used in conjunction with **Distance-measuring Equipment (DME),** described on pages 202–206, or the RMI (p. 211). The accuracy of bearings obtained by VOR is usually regarded as ±2°, although radials may be bent or waved by irregular terrain within the area covered by the VOR. Where possible, these pattern errors are listed in the various publications dealing with radio navigation charts (e.g. Aerad, Jeppesen and others issued by ICAO member states). Maximum ranges and effective heights are listed for each VOR station in these publications and at no time should an attempt be made to rely upon information provided by the equipment when the aircraft is outside these limits.

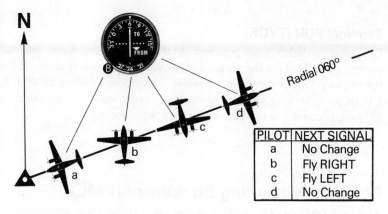

PILOT	NEXT SIGNAL
a	No Change
b	Fly RIGHT
c	Fly LEFT
d	No Change

Fig. 67   When crossing a common radial (in this case 060°) aircraft 'a', 'b', 'c' and 'd' obtain the same VOR indication irrespective of heading. Aircraft 'a' will receive '060° TO' after the VOR station has been overflown.

Safeguards

VOR Transmitters. If for any reason bearings (as measured at the VOR site) wander by more than one degree, an automatic monitor will switch off the installation. A reserve transmitter is usually provided at most sites against possible failure of the main transmitter. **Airborne Equipment.** A failure of the NAV receiver or the omni-bearing Indicator will cause a **No Signal Flag** to appear adjacent to the vertical needle. The flag will also be displayed when out of range of the VOR selected on the receiver or during a failure of the VOR itself.

Doppler VOR (DVOR)

At low levels variation in terrain of differing absorption will often 'bend' VOR radials. While in many cases this presents nothing more serious than an unexpected FLY LEFT or FLY RIGHT command, which may correct itself after a short period, there are instances where unacceptable navigational errors are present.

The older type of VOR transmitter is now being replaced by an improved version which uses the Doppler principle, such a facility being known as DVOR. As far as the pilot is concerned the only difference between VOR and DVOR is the enhanced accuracy of the latter.

Terminal VOR (TVOR)

On some airfields low powered VOR transmitters have been conveniently sited for the purpose of providing azimuth guidance to the runway. Unlike the more expensive Instrument Landing System TVOR provides no glidepath information. However, it is a valuable aid and, because it is used at short range, very accurate.

Distance Measuring Equipment (DME)

Although DME may be used on its own or in conjunction with other aids, it is primarily associated with VOR, when it forms a combined navigational system known as VOR/DME. As such it provides positions in bearing and distance form. DME is a pulse aid operating in the region of 1000 MHz (pulse transmission was described on pp. 179–181), the information being presented on a digital indicator as opposed to the cathode ray tube usually associated with radar.

VOR transmitters offering DME facilities are marked with an appropriate symbol on radio navigation charts (see the Legend Card, Appendix II). Usually the DME receiver has its own ON/OFF switch and a volume control for use while checking the identification signal. This will be the same letters as its accompanying VOR but transmitted at a higher pitch.

DME frequencies are, for convenience, paired with those allocated to VOR: selection of the required VOR automatically switches in the associated DME frequency.

The DME ground facility situated at the VOR site is called a **Responder.** It is similar in function to the airborne Transponder mentioned on page 230, in so far as it remains dormant until triggered by a coded signal from a DME equipment aircraft. The responder will accept signals from up to 100 aircraft simultaneously.

Associated Airborne Equipment

An **Interrogator** carried in the aircraft transmits coded pulses on the frequency relating to the VOR/DME selected by the pilot. When the signal is received at the VOR site the responder transmits back to the aircraft (on a different frequency) a similar coded pulse. This is received by the interrogator during intervals in its transmission, i.e. between pulses. Time-lapse between the pulse from the aircraft and its return from the Responder is measured electronically by the Interrogator and converted into a nautical mile display.

Like most radio equipment there are several versions of DME, each differing in detail design and the facilities provided. DME sets intended for light single- and twin-engined aircraft sometimes present information on an electronic digital display. Facilities which may be selected on a switch provided for the purpose are:

Distance to or from the facility

Groundspeed to or from the facility

Time to overhead the facility

The equipment provides groundspeed or a time to overhead the facility by computing the rate at which range is altering, but it can only give accurate groundspeed, or time-to-beacon information when the aircraft is flying towards or away from the VOR/DME and not, for example, when the ground station is being maintained at a steady distance to one side of the aircraft. A typical self-contained DME is illustrated in Fig. 68.

Although DME may vary in detail here are some of the features likely to be found on modern equipment:

ON/OFF/VOLUME for use in identifying the DME.

NAV1/NAV2 When two NAV receivers are fitted in the aircraft this switch enables the pilot to obtain DME information from either of the VORs being received, assuming they are paired with a DME.

11 The Radio Aids

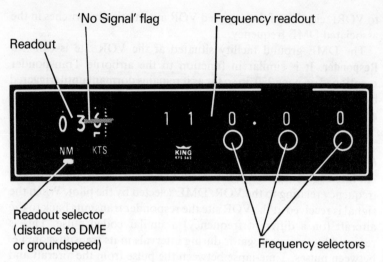

Fig. 68 King DME with independent frequency selection. Readout may be 'distance to DME' or 'groundspeed' according to the position of the readout selector.

FACILITY SWITCH When fitted the following positions may be provided:

ET This gives Elapsed Time on final approach, a position which may be used during an ILS procedure (pp. 129–138). In effect this part of the equipment is an electronic stopwatch.

TTS Time to Station. Some DME provides simultaneous readouts for groundspeed, time to station and distance to station. Consequently there is no need for a TTS switch.

GS Groundspeed. (See comments for TTS.)

GMT In this position the time is indicated.

ETA When the aircraft is flying towards a DME station an ETA can be obtained in this position.

HOLD It is sometimes convenient to hold the last readouts displayed while changing to another DME. When HOLD is selected the equipment will freeze its last readings until NAV1 or NAV2 are selected.

RNAV Used with Area Nav. based on VOR/DME.

Earlier DME sets required a warm-up period during which readings fluctuated random fashion while the interrogator searched before locking onto the ground based responder. Modern DME is ready for use very quickly and station 'lock-on' requires less than 1 second. The example illustrated in Fig. 69 gives DISTANCE to station, GROUNDSPEED and a digital repeat of the VOR reading.

Accuracy

Typical slant range accuracy is ±0.1 n.m. and ±5% for groundspeed and TTS.

Developments

The main limitations of DME are that at high altitudes range near the DME station it is inaccurate due to slant range considerations. Also the groundspeed and time to station facilities of the equipment may only be enjoyed while flying directly to or from the station.

Some of the avionics manufacturers have developed navigation systems based upon a computer and mention should be made of the DME function of the system. After raw DME information has been fed to the computer allowance is made for:

(a) aircraft height and distance from the station so that slant range is converted to ground range.

Distance to DME readout   Groundspeed / Radial readout

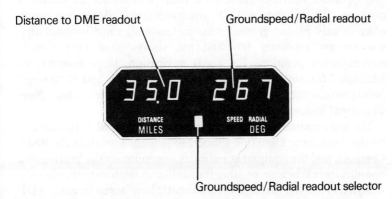

Groundspeed / Radial readout selector

Fig. 69   King KI 267 DME Indicator with electronic readout giving 'distance to DME' on the left and a choice of 'groundspeed' or 'VOR Radial' which may be selected on a two-position switch. DME frequency is automatically set with VOR selection.

(b) aircraft heading relative to the DME station is used to correct groundspeed and time to station readouts which would otherwise only be accurate while flying directly to or from the responder.

At present such installations are normally only fitted to larger twin-engined aircraft but considering the rapid development of electronics and its continued miniaturization, it is likely to find its way into single-engine aircraft.

Safeguards

In the case of mechanical Veeder counter readouts (i.e. of a type similar to a car mileage indicator) a red warning flag will appear across the numbers when the DME is out of range or a fault has occurred. Most modern equipment embodies an electronic digital readout which will remain blank when there is a failure.

Automatic Direction Finding (ADF)

Equipment similar to the manual D/F sets described earlier at one time formed part of an aircraft's radio installation. The navigator would transfer two or more radio bearings onto his chart (making due allowance for the distance flown in the time interval between the first and last bearing) to produce a **Running Fix,** i.e. the point where two or more bearings cross on a chart to indicate an aircraft's position. This airborne D/F equipment was dependent upon conveniently placed ground transmitters and, since broadcasting stations are relatively few and not always sited in the most advantageous positions for aerial navigation, large numbers of additional transmitters were installed near airfields and at strategic points within the Airway and Control Zone complex. These **Non-directional Beacons** are described in the next section.

The old manually operated loop has been replaced in the aircraft by the Automatic Direction Finder, sometimes known as the **Radio Compass,** and the equipment indicates continuously the bearing of a non-directional beacon or other transmitter in relation to the aircraft.

Signals received through the automatic loop aerial in early ADF equipment were phased to control a small electric motor which continued to rotate the loop until a null was reached. A fixed aerial on the aircraft provided automatic 'sensing'. The pointer on a remote-reading bearing indicator or radio compass moved in unison with the loop, continuously indicating the direction of the NDB. Homings to an NDB can be made by flying with the radio compass needle pointing to the lubber line marked on the instrument, the lubber line representing the nose of the aircraft. Fig. 70 shows in simplified form the main components of an ADF set and their functions.

To simplify explanation the old type of equipment with a rotating loop aerial is illustrated. Modern ADF installations use a fixed, flush-mounted aerial which is based on a ferrite core. There are no moving parts.

Non-directional Beacons

Operating in the MF band and transmitting in all directions, the NDB emits a continuous wave.

Most NDBs are tone modulated at 400 c/s. (Some beacons controlled by Trinity House and sited in coastal regions of the UK are tone modulated at 1052 cycles, but these, as well as conveniently located broadcast stations, may be used by the radio compass.) A two-or three-letter identification signal is at intervals superimposed in morse on the 400-cycle note. In some regions the profusion of NDB installations has made close spacing of their frequencies unavoidable and the identification signal enables a pilot to ensure that he has tuned to the correct beacon.

The NDB has a range of 10 to 100 n.m. or more, according to the power of the transmitter, which in turn is determined by the use for which the beacon is provided. A beacon sited as an aid to airways flying would have a long range as opposed to **Locators,** low-powered NDBs intended primarily as a means of guiding the aircraft to a suitable position in preparation for an instrument approach at an airport.

Not all non-directional beacons transmit an audible tone interrupted by a two or three letter identification in morse. Some emit carrier wave signals only, a toneless hiss that was described under **Audio Frequencies** (page 177). The advantage of this arrangement is that in areas where radio frequencies are closely spaced such a transmitter is likely to cause less interference should it break through, for example, a domestic broadcast or other station. So that the pilot may identify the NDB there is provision in the ADF receiver to add tone when required, a facility known as a **Beat Frequency Oscillator (BFO).**

Obviously a pilot selecting an NDB for navigational purposes must be able to identify if it is **Tone Modulated** (known as A2 transmission)

11 The Radio Aids

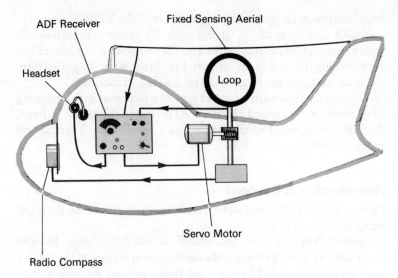

Fig. 70 Relationship of principal ADF components. For purpose of explanation old type equipment is illustrated; modern ADF no longer includes a loop aerial rotated by an electric motor.

or **Without Voice** (A1 transmission, i.e. unmodulated). Methods of showing the information on radio charts are explained on page 106. Whenever an NDB is shown on the radio navigation chart to be carrier wave only (no voice), the beat frequency oscillator will have to be switched on.

Associated Airborne Equipment

The aircraft installation is made up of the following components:

1. An ADF receiver.
2. An automatic loop aerial.
3. A fixed aerial for automatic 'sensing'.
4. One or more ADF Indicators (Radio Compass).

1. ADF Receiver (Fig. 71)

Although the various makes of equipment differ in detail, their general principle remains the same. ADF receivers work in the MF band and while older designs were continuously tuned like a domestic radio, most equipment is now crystal controlled and digital

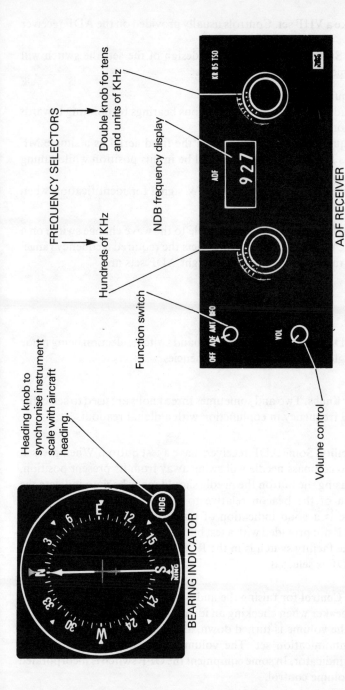

FREQUENCY SELECTORS

Double knob for tens and units of KHz

NDB frequency display

Hundreds of KHz

Function switch

KR 85 TSO

ADF

9 2 7

OFF ADF ANT BFO

VOL

ADF RECEIVER

Heading knob to synchronise instrument scale with aircraft heading.

Volume control

HDG

BEARING INDICATOR

Fig. 71   King KR 85 ADF receiver with digital tuning. The ADF Indicator has an adjustable scale to provide QDMs to the beacon without need of addition. Needle response is tested by selecting ANT on the function switch when the bearing will read 090° . The needle should swing positively towards the NDB when 'ADF' is re-selected.

tuned like a VHF set. Controls usually provided on the ADF receiver are:

Facility Switch. According to the design of the set, the switch will have some or all of these positions:

OFF: equipment inoperative.
ADF: radio compass gives continuous bearings by pointing towards the station selected.
REC: equipment operates through the fixed aerial as a simple MF receiver. The facility switch should be in this position while tuning and identifying a station.
BFO: gives audible signal from CW signal for identification when beacon is not tone modulated.

Frequency Band Switch. Comparable to the wave change switch on a domestic radio set, this control selects the required frequency range. Typical ranges on modern lightweight ADF sets are:

Range 1   190–440 kHz
Range 2   420–900 kHz
Range 3   850–1750 kHz

Some ADF receivers do not have a band switch, selection being made on a single range covering all frequencies.

Selector Knobs. Two and sometimes three knobs are used to select the required frequency in conjunction with a digital readout.

Test Facility. Some ADF receivers have a test button. When pressed the radio compass needle will swing away from its present position. On releasing the button the needle should move back to indicate the direction of the beacon relative to the aircraft. Speed of needle response is a good indication of signal strength. When the ADF receiver is not provided with a test button the needle will move to 090° when the facility switch is in the REC position. It will remain there until ADF is selected.

Volume Control for raising the audio output through the headset or cabin speaker when checking an identification signal. After identification the volume is turned down, allowing full undisturbed use of the communication set. The volume control does not affect the bearing indicator. In some equipment the OFF switch is incorporated in the volume control.

2 & 3. Automatic Loop Aerial and Fixed Aerial

The automatic loop provides direction finding information for the ADF receiver. Early loops were surrounded by streamlined housings for installation above or below the fuselage, but it was later the practice to reduce drag by using ADF loops of the suppressed type which fitted flush to the skin of the aircraft. These have no moving parts.

4. Bearing Indicator (Fig. 71)

Because the automatic loop is often installed some distance from the pilot, provision must be made for a remote-reading bearing indicator. The needle of the ADF Indicator remains synchronized with the loop aerial, indicating the bearing to the NDB relative to the fore and aft axis of the aeroplane. Additional bearing indicators may be provided for other crew members.

Radio Magnetic Indicator (RMI)

So far only the simple case of an aircraft homing onto a transmitter has been mentioned in this chapter, but ADF has other applications. For example, the position of an aircraft can be established when a bearing from a known origin crosses another such bearing. It should be remembered that while the needle of the radio compass points towards the transmitter continuously, the scale against which it moves is fixed to the aircraft, so that all bearings indicated by the instrument are relative to the fore and aft axis of the aeroplane. To determine the magnetic bearing from the aircraft to the NDB (in other words the QDM) it is necessary to add the magnetic heading being flown at the time to the radio compass reading (Fig. 33, page 105).

This procedure is rendered unnecessary when a **Radio Magnetic Indicator (RMI)** is fitted in place of the standard radio compass, because the RMI gives bearings based upon information from two sources:

(a) Magnetic compass headings, fed into the instrument from the aircraft's distant reading compass, rotate the scale.
(b) Bearings from the ADF (or VOR) set move the needle against the scale mentioned in (a).

The RMI is thus able to provide simultaneous readings:

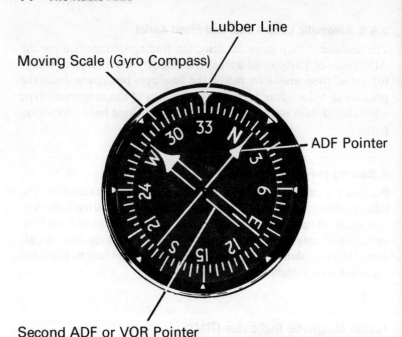

Fig. 72 The Radio Magnetic Indicator (RMI) scale is linked to the compass system so that QDMs are indicated without need of adding Magnetic Heading to ADF Indicator reading. Illustration shows an aircraft heading of 330°M and a QDM to the NDB of 012°.

(a) Magnetic headings from the distant reading compass. These are read against a lubber line on the instrument.
(b) QDM to a known NDB. This is provided by the needle, which is read against the moving scale controlled by the distant reading compass (Fig. 70).
(c) QDM of a second NDB or more usually a VOR.

A simple and inexpensive method of providing magnetic bearings without the need for adding aircraft heading to radio compass reading, one now often fitted to light aircraft, takes the form of an adjustable instrument scale. Using the knob provided the pilot sets the magnetic heading being flown on the DI against the ADF Indicator lubber line when the ADF needle will provide continuous QDMs, to the NDB being received. When the aircraft alters heading the ADF Indicator scale must likewise be adjusted (page 107).

Use and Limitations

In common with most aircraft radio equipment ADF sets have in recent years become lighter in weight and simpler in operation, a typical example suitable for small aircraft being illustrated in Fig. 71. It will be seen that the facility switch on this set is limited to OFF, ADF, ANT (normal MF receiver) and BFO (page 207), but the equipment is nevertheless capable of adequate performance.

The performance to be expected from ADF under normal conditions is as follows:

Range:	when tuned to an NDB	10–100 n.m.
	when tuned to a powerful broadcast station	200 n.m.
Accuracy:	High-powered beacon Day	±1°
	Night	±2°
	Low-powered beacon	±2½°

Conditions Affecting the Accuracy of ADF

The radiation pattern of radio waves is distorted when signals are transmitted over areas of widely varying electric conductivity, and although reception may remain satisfactory, directional properties will often be disturbed. In so far as it affects the operation of ADF, the errors caused by varying conductivity are:

Coastal Effect (Fig. 73)

When ADF is used over the sea, bearings crossing the coastline at an angle of less than 60° are bent towards the coast, causing the radio compass to give an inaccurate reading. The degree of bearing error is dependent among other factors upon the angle at which it crosses the coast and 30 degrees or less should be considered unreliable. Coastal effect may be minimized by:

(a) Flying at a greater altitude.
(b) Choosing beacons or other transmitters which are likely to provide bearings crossing the coast at an angle of between 60° and 90°. The shaded portion on Fig. 73 denotes the area of accuracy for the particular case illustrated.

High Terrain Effect

Mountainous areas can absorb and reflect radio waves, causing inaccurate radio compass readings. Like coast effect, errors resulting

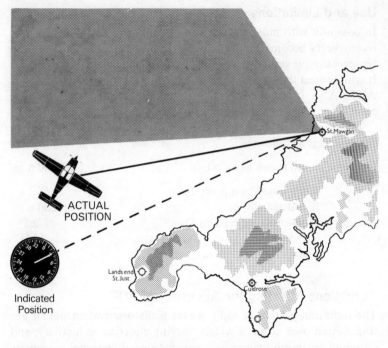

Fig. 73   Coastal Effect is avoided when bearings leave the coast at an
angle of 60° or more, i.e. within the shaded area.

from high ground may be minimized by climbing to a greater altitude
when traffic conditions permit.

Quadrantal Error (Fig. 74)

Bearings approaching the automatic loop at a small angle to the wing
or fuselage will be bent towards the structure of the aircraft, causing
an inaccurate reading in a manner similar to coastal effect.
Quadrantal error on each heading may be determined by conducting
a radio compass swing (similar to the usual magnetic compass swing).
The loop may then be compensated, leaving a small residual error
which is unlikely to affect the usefulness of the aid.

Thunderstorms

Large displacements of the ADF needle are likely when thunderstorms are present; the equipment may home on to the electric storm
in preference to the required NDB. Serious accidents have in the past
resulted from this limitation and ADF must be used with discretion,

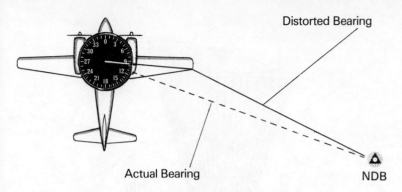

Fig. 74   Quadrantal Error caused by the aircraft structure.

constantly relating the ADF indicator to the direction indicator and whatever other equipment is in the aircraft.

Night Effect

This was explained on page 192. Like MF and HF D/F, accuracy of the ADF loop deteriorates when nightfall causes the sky waves to return to earth at a steeper angle. The lower the frequency of the NDB, the less it will be affected since in this waveband the ground wave is predominant (p. 171 and Fig. 49).

Mis-tuning

The need to provide a great number of beacons has in certain parts of the world resulted in the close spacing of their frequencies (p. 207). Should the ADF receiver be tuned inaccurately, two stations may be received, when the radio compass will take up a position which lies somewhere between the two transmitters (with a bias towards the stronger signal). It is therefore important to tune the ADF with the facility switch in the REC position when signals are brought in on the fixed aerial. Ideally, the identification signal of the required beacon only should be heard, but when it cannot be tuned to maximum signal strength without a break-through from another station, it is sometimes preferable to off-tune slightly away from the interfering transmitter. Most digital tuned ADF receivers adjust in steps of 1 kHz. Consequently when the required NDB has a frequency of, say, 378.5 kHz the equipment can only be tuned to within 0.5 kHz. In the example given here the pilot should try 378 and 379 to find the most satisfactory setting.

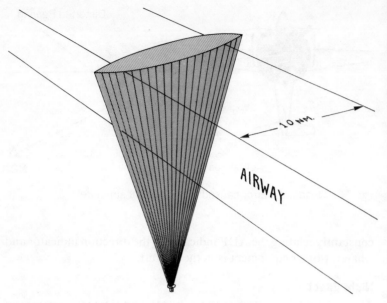

Fig. 75   Fan Marker.

Fan Markers

A single ADF installation indicates the position of an aircraft only when it overflies the NDB (or other transmitter). At this point the radio compass needle will swing widely before setting onto a new heading of 180° or so, indicating that the transmitter is behind the aircraft.

When for control purposes it is necessary for a pilot to report his position before reaching the NDB, a separate transmitter is sometimes used. Operating on a frequency of 75 MHz, these **Fan Markers** transmit a high-pitched (3000 cycles) identification signal in the form of repeated dots and/or dashes. Fan markers are usually located within airways and their aerial systems are arranged to radiate a narrow vertical fan-shaped beam which extends across the width of the airway like a curtain drawn across a corridor. The thickness of the beam is limited and aircraft flying through the fan marker receive its signals for a relatively brief period, thus ensuring that a position report can be given with accuracy (Fig. 75).

Fan markers are received in the aircraft on a separate **Marker Receiver** which provides two indications when the aircraft is over the reporting points:

1. A high-pitched coded signal delivered through the pilot's headset or the cabin speaker.
2. A flashing light on the marker receiver indicator panel. This is illustrated in Fig. 80 on page 225.

The marker receiver is also used in conjunction with ILS, a landing aid described later in the chapter. It should be remembered that switching on the ADF receiver does not automaticaly include the marker receiver, which is controlled by a separate switch.

While the advent of more modern radio aids has considerably reduced the number of fan markers, ADF continues to play an important rôle in radio navigation, both as a short range locator for instrument approaches and as an *en route* navigational aid in areas where VHF limitations preclude the satisfactory siting of VOR. Since the NDB is relatively inexpensive it is often sited at small airfields for use as a homer.

Instrument Landing System (ILS)

ILS is a pilot-interpreted aid, i.e. information is provided in the form of visual indications upon which the pilot can make his own decisions as opposed to the type of aid where instructions are given from the ground.

Previously, the function now served by ILS was performed by an older system called **Standard Beam Approach (SBA).** Developed from Lorenz, an early German radio aid, SBA presented its information to the pilot in the form of aural signals which told him when he was lined up with the centre of the runway during the approach or if he was to left or right. Whereas SBA operated on HF, Instrument Landing System is a VHF aid. Its main advantages over SBA may be summarized as follows:

1. All indications are visual and without ambiguity.
2. The aircraft's position in relation to an ideal guide path for the particular runway is continuously displayed.
3. It is relatively easy to use and very accurate, small deviations from runway centre and/or glide path producing large indications on the instrument.

The airfield equipment is based upon two main transmitters known as the **Localizer** and **Glide Path.** These are augmented by two (or, very occasionally, three) **Marker Beacons** situated at a convenient distance from the runway threshold.

Localizer Transmitter (Fig. 76)

The localizer transmits a signal in the 108–112 MHz band through an aerial system situated at the upwind end of the runway. The aerial is accurately beamed to radiate two distinct patterns, each modulated at a different pitch. The right-hand sector transmits a 150-cycle note and the left sector emits a 90-cycle note. The complete pattern may be imagined as two searchlights, their adjacent edges overlapping to produce a 5° beam which is directed along the centre line of the runway and continued downwind to form an accurate approach. An aircraft flying down the centre of the beam will receiver RIGHT and LEFT signals (150 and 90 c/s respectively) at equal intensities, the relative strengths of the two signals varying according to its disposition left or right of the centre line. Outside the 5° beam reception is 150 c/s (right of runway heading) or 90 c/s (left of runway heading). The beam and its flanking 150 c/s and 90 c/s sectors may be received at a range of up to 25 n.m. from the localizer transmitter according to the height of the aircraft. A two-or three-letter identification signal is transmitted at intervals in morse.

Associated Airborne Equipment

The localizer receiver in the aircraft may be devoted entirely to ILS, although it is now usually the practice to include ILS frequencies in the NAV receiver used for VOR reception. Whereas VOR operates by phase comparison, ILS is based upon tone comparison between the 90 and 150 c/s sectors.

When tuned to an ILS frequency the NAV receiver feeds signals from the localizer to the **ILS indicator** (Fig. 78, p. 222).

This instrument, which forms the primary ILS display converts RIGHT and LEFT signals into left and right deflections of the vertical or localizer needle, i.e. in a corrective sense. Four dots either side of a central circle provide a scale for the localizer needle, a 4-dot deflection indicating the extreme edge of the beam or approximately $2\frac{1}{2}°$ to one side of its centre line. Figure 76 on p. 219 will show that when flying in the landing direction ILS indications are interpreted as instructions to attain the centre of the beam, e.g. needle to the left – FLY LEFT: needle to the right – FLY RIGHT; the change in heading in each case being dependent upon the number of dots left or right indicated by the instrument. Although the sense of these indications is reversed while flying on a reciprocal heading in relation to the landing direction (top left aeroplane in Fig. 76), the pilot can

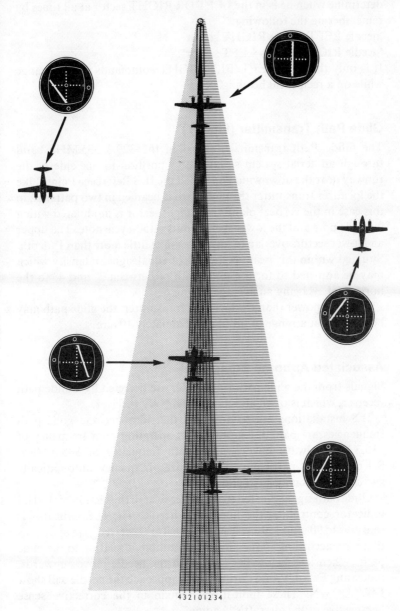

Fig. 76   ILS Localizer transmitter and associated instrument indications
(Glidepath needle omitted for clarity).

determine when he is in the LEFT OR RIGHT sector at all times by remembering the following:

'needle LEFT means RIGHT sector'

'needle RIGHT means LEFT sector'

It is only the FLY LEFT/FLY RIGHT commands which change while on a reciprocal heading.

Glide Path Transmitter (Fig. 77)

The Glide Path transmits a signal in the 329.3–335 MHz band through an aerial system situated at a position to one side of the runway near the downwind end called the **ILS Reference Point.** Like the localizer transmitter the glide path is beamed in two patterns, in this case in the vertical plane. The upper sector is modulated with a 90-cycle note and the lower sector emits a 150-cycle note. The upper and lower sectors overlap to form a beam of little more than 1° depth. Situated within this beam is the line of equal signal intensity which may be adjusted to form a glide path of between 2° and 4° to the horizontal, 3° being an average setting.

Of lower power than the localizer transmitter, the glide path may be received at a range of up to approximately 10 n.m.

Associated Airborne Equipment

Signals from the glide path transmitter are detected by a glide path receiver, which is often attached to the NAV receiver.

ILS installations are so arranged that localizer and glide path frequencies are paired, e.g. localizers operating on a frequency of 110.3 MHz always have a glide path frequency of 335.0 MHz. Selection of a particular ILS localizer frequency automatically switches in the associated glide path.

Glide path signals are fed from the receiver to the section of the ILS indicator controlling the horizontal needle. The ILS indicator is sensitive to 90- and 150-cycle notes which are received in proportions that vary according to the aircraft's position in relation to the glide path. When it is below the glide path the needle moves upwards, indicating FLY UP, and during a high approach the needle will show FLY DOWN. These indications remain in the corrective sense irrespective of the aircraft's heading.

The glide path needle has a vertical scale composed of four dots above and four dots below the central circle on the instrument face (Fig. 78). Translated into terms of aircraft displacement above or

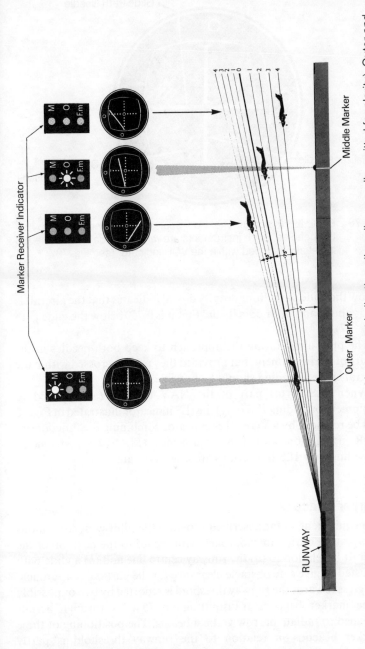

Fig. 77 ILS Glidepath transmitter and associated instrument indications (Localizer needle omitted for clarity). Outer and Middle Marker beacons are shown with their related Marker Receiver displays (see Fig. 80).

221

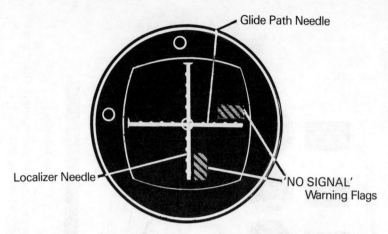

Fig. 78   Basic ILS Indicator. The 4-dot scales are partly obscured by the needles. Such instruments are rare these days because ILS is usually included within the VOR indicator (see Fig. 79).

below the glide path, 'four dots fly down' indicates that the aircraft is 0.45° above and 'four dots fly up' that it is 0.75° below the glide path (Fig. 77).

The pilot aims during the approach to keep both needles in the centre of the instrument, but provided they remain crossed within the central circle a landing should be possible.

When ILS forms part of the NAV receiver (as opposed to equipment providing ILS only) the ILS indicator illustrated in Fig. 78 will be replaced by a VOR/ILS indicator combining the functions of VOR navigation and ILS approaches (Fig. 79). Instruments providing only ILS indications are now very rare.

Marker Beacons

The equipment so far described provides the pilot with continuous information during the approach with regard to the position of the aircraft in relation to (a) the runway centre line and (b) a glide path adjusted to give safe obstacle clearance for the particular approach. Progress towards the runway threshold is reported by two or possibly three marker beacons transmitting on 75 MHz through aerials designed to radiate narrow vertical beams. The positioning of these marker beacons in relation to the runway threshold is partly dependent upon the availability of suitable sites, but the following

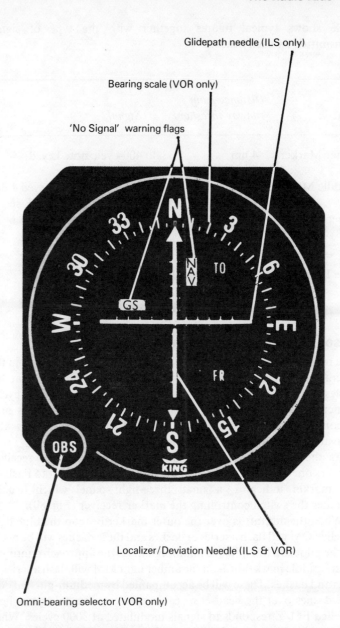

Glidepath needle (ILS only)

Bearing scale (VOR only)

'No Signal' warning flags

Localizer/Deviation Needle (ILS & VOR)

Omni-bearing selector (VOR only)

Fig. 79   Combined VOR/ILS Indicator shown full size. Glidepath needle comes into operation whenever an ILS frequency is selected on the NAV receiver.

table shows typical figures together with the type of signal transmitted by each beacon.

Beacon	Distance from runway threshold	Signal
Outer Marker	4 nm	400-cycle note keyed 2 dashes/sec.
Middle Marker	3500 ft	1,300-cycle note keyed 1 dot and one dash per $\frac{2}{3}$ sec.
Inner Marker	250 ft	3,000-cycle note keyed 6 dots/sec.

The Inner Marker Beacon is rarely installed at civil airports.

Associated Airborne Equipment

The marker receiver, a small unit tuned to 75 MHz, is carried in the aircraft, its circuit designed to respond to signals modulated at 400 cycles (Outer Marker), 1300 cycles (Middle Marker), and 3000 cycles (Inner Marker). As already explained, the inner marker is now uncommon, but the 3000-cycle response of the receiver is also activated by fan markers mentioned on p. 216).

As the aircraft overflies a marker beacon the signal received triggers one of the three circuits, causing a coloured light to flash on the marker indicator, a small three-light panel which usually includes the switch controlling the marker receiver (Fig. 80).

When the aircraft is over the outer marker beacon the blue light labelled OM will flash a series of dashes and these dashes will be heard by the pilot as a low-pitched audio signal. As the approach continues to the middle marker beacon the amber light MM will flash a series of dots and dashes. These will be accompanied by medium-pitched dots and dashes over the headset or cabin speaker. The colourless light labelled FM/Z responds to signals modulated at 3000 cycles. When an inner marker beacon forms part of the airport ILS installation this light will flash a series of dots as the aircraft passes overhead and these will be heard as a high-pitched signal. More usually this light reacts to signals received from fan marker beacons. These coded beacons are an aid to navigation (see p. 216) and as such form no part of the ILS system.

The 3-light visual indicator can be mounted in the vertical or horizontal position and the intensity of the lights may be reduced for night flying. For test purposes each bulb in the type illustrated may be lighted by pressing its glass cover.

Since ILS is a visual aid the audio signals from the marker receiver are incidental to the three-light presentations. The control switch on the three-light visual indicator panel usually enables the pilot to reduce the strength of the audio signals or mute them entirely.

Safeguards

Localizer, Glide Path, and Marker Beacon Transmitters

Most ILS installations at modern airports have provision for self-monitoring, i.e. receivers are positioned on the ground to detect any departure from acceptable limits of beam accuracy, reduction in transmitting power or complete failure of one or more of the transmitters. An automatic alarm system alerts the appropriate airfield personnel to the nature of the fault and in some cases brings into operation a standby transmitter.

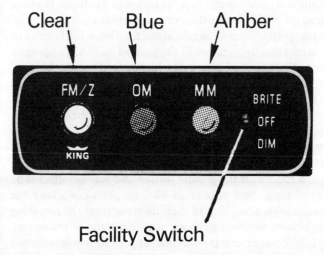

Fig. 80   King KR 22 Marker Beacon Receiver. The Facility Switch
provides ON/OFF, brightness control and a lamp test.

Airborne Equipment

The most serious case would be failure of the localizer or glide path receiver, such an incident being indicated on the ILS indicator. When a receiver ceases to provide information, either as a result of its own malfunction or a failure of the ground installation, a **No Signal Flag** will appear adjacent to the affected needle (Fig. 78), which will itself remain in the neutral position. The no signal flags will also operate when the aircraft is out of ILS range. Failure of the marker receiver is of less consequence and needs no explanation. Two complete installations are often carried in the aircraft as an insurance against failure of the receivers and displays.

Developments

ILS will gradually be replaced by **Microwave Landing System (MLS)** which, among other advantages, can allow approaches to the runway from a number of angles instead of the present 'straight in' approach from a distance of 5 or more miles.

At a number of airfields DME (page 202) is installed and when this is used in conjunction with ILS the pilot is presented with a constant distance to runway threshold.

Surveillance Radar Element (SRE)

Pulse transmission and its display on the screen of a cathode ray tube was discussed on p. 179. It was then explained that an echo or 'blip' could be made to appear on a range scale or time base, the bottom of the scale representing the position of the ground station. The greater the distance to the reflecting object, the higher up the scale the 'blip' will appear. Transmission of the pulse and reception of the echo was in this case effected by a fixed reflector type aerial. If such an aerial is rotated in azimuth through 360° it can be made to **Scan** the area surrounding the ground station and the resulting display would then take the form of a luminous radius line sweeping around the face of the cathode ray tube in unison with the revolving aerial. The centre of the screen now represents the ground station and echoes reflected by objects within range will appear in various positions along the revolving range scale according to their distance from the revolving aerial, close objects producing echoes near the centre of the screen. Conversely, objects at or near the extreme range of the equipment will cause the revolving range scale to deposit a 'blip' near the edge of the tube. The aerial is rotated at 30 RPM (or faster in the case of some equipment), so that in effect the revolving trace will 'paint' a picture on the screen at a rate of 30 times a minute, the picture being held during sweeps by a suitable fluorescent coating. The screen is usually etched with a series of concentric range circles and a compass rose, so enabling the position of any echo to be determined in bearing and distance form. A radar set of this kind is called a **Plan Position Indicator (PPI)** and a simple example is illustrated in Fig. 81.

The elevation angle of the radar aerial is adjustable so that high- and low-flying aircraft may be located. In the low position permanent echoes will be received from buildings, trees and high ground, the resultant 'clutter' on the screen tending to swamp echoes from aircraft flying low on the horizon or those on approach to the runway. In modern radar equipment permanent echoes are reduced to a minimum by the introduction of a circuit called a 'moving target indicator'.

Angled upwards to sweep the surrounding airspace, the aerial will detect aircraft flying at a higher elevation in relation to the station, but the prime feature of the PPI is its ability to display aircraft in their correct positions relative to the ground station. The equipment is known as **Surveillance Radar** and as such it may be used to guide aircraft through the swept area, if necessary towards an airfield.

Having located an aircraft and directed it to a convenient position within 8–10 n.m. range of the runway, the task of following the echo will be transferred to a screen with an expanded scale, i.e. **Approach Radar,** its purpose being to guide the aircraft within close limits of accuracy during a final approach in IMC. The screen is etched with an extended runway centre line marked off in distances to the threshold so that the controller is able to inform the pilot of distance to the point of touch-down and disposition left or right of the runway centre line. Early equipment, known as GCA (Ground Controlled Approach), was housed in a mobile caravan positioned at the end of the runway. The caravan and its crew moved to another site whenever the landing direction changed. GCA has now been replaced by an improved form of equipment which is not only more compact, but has the advantage that it may be worked by a single operator and may be electronically offset to the centreline of any runway for which it has been calibrated.

Surveillance Approach Radar

Approach radar is the general term covering the services provided by an approach radar unit up to a limit of 40 miles from an airfield traffic zone, although in practice this range may be much greater.

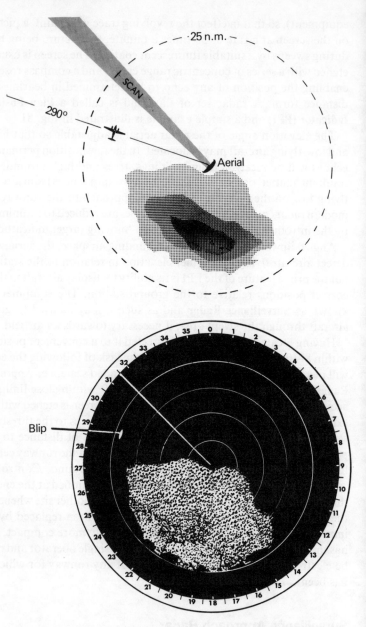

Fig. 81   Plan Position Indicator (PPI) showing an aircraft bearing 290°
          from the radar station at a range of 19 nm (lower picture).
          Note the permanent echoes from high ground shown
          in the upper illustration.

Aircraft requiring radar guidance and approach assistance are monitored by the radar unit and directed to some convenient position in relation to the airfield and in range of the airfield approach radar (also known as **short range radar**).

Originating from an aerial rotating through 360°, the display appears on a PPI cathode ray tube depicting the path of the aircraft in plan form against the extended runway centre line. The screen is marked in ranges to the runway threshold at intervals of ½ mile with related advisory heights.

Throughout the approach, information is passed by the Talk-down controller (alternatively known as the Talk-down director) to the pilot in plain language and a typical surveillance radar approach is detailed in Chapter 8, p. 142). Additional to its **Permanent Echo Supressor** (a design feature for the purpose of reducing unwanted echoes from buildings, high terrain, etc.), the equipment embodies a circuit designed to reduce scatter from rain and cloud.

In order to take advantage of secondary radar the aircraft must carry a transponder (p. 230). Modern ground equipment is designed to integrate the aircraft's responder signal providing instant identification, together with a digital Flight-Level read-out.

Associated Airborne Equipment

The minimum requirement in the aircraft is a communication set on which to receive instructions from the radar unit. Obviously, large metal aircraft will produce a more powerful echo than small wooden airframes. Particularly when heavy rain or cloud formations are present, performance of the ground equipment is markedly improved when a transponder is fitted in the aircraft. The coded echoes from transponders make it possible to readily identify a particular aircraft on the screen and provision is sometimes made for the cruising altitude to be included in the trace. In the absence of a transponder, aircraft requesting radar service will usually be required to turn onto a particular heading for identification and VDF may be used for the purpose of confirmation. Only suitably equipped radar stations are able to make use of transponder echoes.

Accuracy

Errors in the equipment are negligible, so that accuracy is largely dependent upon the skill of the talk-down controller and the ability of the pilot to follow his instructions.

The ATC Transponder (Secondary Radar)

In addition to the problems of echoes being swamped by heavy rain or large cloud formations, the growth of air traffic has made it increasingly difficult for controllers to identify individual aircraft on the radar screen. Furthermore, it has always been necessary for pilots to turn through a number of degrees for identification (sometimes VDF is used to assist identification) but such a procedure is time consuming and inconvenient. The transponder overcomes these problems by sending back to the ground station an amplified echo when a pulse has been received. While transponders differ in detailed design, the following text should enable the student to understand how to use this valuable equipment, which has assumed great importance with the growth of air traffic.

The transponder has a switch usually marked OFF, STBY, ON, ALT and TST. There is an IDENT button which enhances the strength of the echo on the radar controller's screen. In the King KT76A transponder illustrated the codes are selected on four knobs, one for each number (Fig. 82).

The Mode Selector

OFF: The transponder is not in use.

STBY: The equipment is warmed up and on standby ready for immediate use. When the controller wants to receive a boosted echo from the transponder, the pilot will be requested to 'squawk' on a particular code.

Fig. 82   King KT 76A Transponder. The code requested by ATC is set on four knobs, each with its numeric display. Below the word IDENT is an 'Ident' push button which will cause the aircraft's 'blip' to intensify on the controller's radar screen to assist identification.

ON: In this position the transponder will receive pulses from the ground and return an echo in a form that gives it identity according to the code selected.

ALT: When an encoding altimeter is fitted this position is used to add the aircraft's flight level to the echo.

IDENT: Further confirmation on aircraft's identity may be obtained by the controller requesting a pilot under radar guidance to 'Squawk Ident' when he will press the IDENT button. This has the effect of intensifying the image on the radar.

Working Principle

Transponders remain dormant until they receive a pulse from the ground-based radar station. The echo takes the form of a **Pulse Train,** gaps between elements being altered according to the code set by the pilot as requested by the controller. On the ground the radar equipment is fitted with a **Pulse Gate** which may likewise be adjusted to the same code as the aircraft. For example, this means that when a controller requests the pilot to 'Squawk four nine zero zero' the ground equipment will reject all echoes other than those with a pulse train relating to 4900. Thus the radar controller is able to identify a particular aircraft. The equipment can identify up to 4096 different codes.

Encoding Altimeters

The use of an encoding altimeter in conjunction with a transponder provides the radar controller with continuous flight level information on the reporting aircraft. This information, which is based on the standard altimeter setting, appears alongside the echo on the radar screen. The **Blind Encoder** is a simple device which may be added to the radio installation. As the name implies, it has no visual readout and its function is to measure pressure and convert this into electronic signals for the transponder which adds the information in the form of flight levels at 100 ft intervals. This type of equipment is usually fitted in light trainers.

More advanced aircraft, particularly those capable of cruising at altitudes above 20,000 ft, will have an altimeter with the usual pilot readout and a built-in encoder. The encoding unit comes into operation when ALT is selected on the mode selector.

Using the Transponder

When changing codes a pilot will obviously pass through a number of others. Since these codes might be interrogating other aircraft at the time, the controller would be presented with a number of unwanted echoes. Therefore STBY (standby) should be selected on the control switch prior to moving the code selectors.

All requests for codes must be read back by the pilot.

Special Purpose Codes have been set aside to warn ATC of unusual circumstances:

Code 7700   To indicate an emergency condition. Aircraft already in contact with an appropriate ATC service will normally remain on the code being used at the time.

Code 7600   To indicate radio failure.

Code 7500   Unless circumstances justify use of Code 7700, this one indicates unlawful interference with the planned flight.

Code 2000   This should be selected when entering UK airspace from an adjacent area where the use of a transponder was not required.

Appendix I
The Flight and Ground Test for the IMC Rating

Holders of an IMC Rating are often relatively inexperienced pilots yet the qualification allows them to fly in or above cloud and out of sight of the ground while carrying non-hire and reward passengers. This will be uppermost in the mind of an examiner while conducting a test for the issue or renewal of the rating.

Although contents of the test are laid down by the CAA there is no formal, line-by-line test form so that its conduct will differ slightly from examiner to examiner. However, test requirements and levels of accuracy to be demonstrated are published in the *Supplement to CAP 53, The Private Pilot's Licence and Associated Ratings* and reproduced in part within this appendix.

The Ground Test

This takes the form of an oral examination of the various subjects listed in the Longman Syllabus of Flying Training for the Private Pilot's Licence and IMC Rating (IMC Rating section) under the heading of:

5 Syllabus for the Technical Examination

The ground subjects are, in the main, explained in this book but some information will be found in Volumes 1 and 2.

At the end of the ground test the examiner will brief the candidate on what will be expected during the flight test. A typical briefing would be as follows:

> 'I want you to assume that the aircraft has been parked in the open overnight under freezing conditions and that this is the first flight of the day. When we walk out to the aircraft please draw my attention to the checks you are making. I would like you to read aloud from an approved checklist during the walk-around and whenever a checklist is required during the flight.'

Although the IMC Rating course includes training in all the approach aids the candidate will only be tested in one of these and he may select the aid to be used. The briefing will continue on the following lines:

'Decision height for the particular approach you have elected to use is at or about cloudbase and the Met Office has forecast a risk of icing at all the altitudes/levels we are likely to use.'

The examiner will agree with the candidate all speeds – climb, cruise, procedural flying (e.g. holds), approach and minimum speed – for any phase of flight.

'After completing the manoeuvres on the full and limited panel I will give you a heading to steer during which you may be required to climb, descend, select and identify navigational aids and interpret the aircraft's position in relation to one or more of these aids. I will also ask you to take up a hold.'

When no published hold is available for the facility selected the examiner may nominate a VOR or an NDB and prescribe the inbound heading to be used. Usually he will have advised ATC prior to the test.

'During the let down you will descend to decision height and maintain it until I advise you to initiate the missed approach procedure. Afterwards we shall become visual and you will carry out a visual circuit assuming a cloudbase of 800 feet and a visibility of approximately 1 nm.'

If a question occurs to you at any time during the briefing interrupt the examiner. Otherwise you may forget the query and it could be important. In any case, the examiner will invite questions.

The candidate will then complete and file a Special VFR flight plan for the test which will normally be of 1 hour 30 min duration. The examiner will want to discuss your preparation of the flight plan, particularly with reference to determination of decision height and your interpretation of the met. information obtained.

Flight Test Requirements

During the flight test for the initial issue of an IMC Rating the candidate will be expected to demonstrate manual instrument flying in the following phases of flight to the level of accuracy listed at the end of this section.

(a) Full Panel Instrument Flying

Straight and level flight at specified speeds
Turns at a given rate
Turns onto given headings
Climbing and descending
Climbing and descending turns
Recovery from unusual attitudes

(b) Limited Panel Instrument Flying

[assuming failure of the Attitude and Direction Indicators]

Straight and level flight
Climbing and descending
Turns onto given headings
Recovery from unusual attitudes

(c) Use of Radio Navigation Aids

Position-finding by using one or more radio-navigation aids, which must include VOR or ADF. Maintenance of a given track based on a pilot-interpreted aid for 10 minutes.

(d) Let Down and Approach to Decision Height and Missed Approach Procedure

Using a pilot-interpreted aid, carry out a recognized instrument approach procedure to Decision Height. At Decision Height carry out the appropriate missed approach procedure. Decision Height is to be calculated using the procedure explained on pages 51–6.

(e) Bad Weather Circuit and Landing

After completion of item (d), the examiner will direct the candidate to a suitable position in the aerodrome area to carry out a visual bad-weather circuit and landing under simulated weather conditions specified by the examiner.

Pilots holding a Multi-engine Rating

When the candidate holds a multi-engine rating and elects to take the test on such an aircraft the following additional items will be included. During this part of the test the examiner may be responsible for navigation and ATC liaison. On resumption of normal flight the candidate will be told the position of the aircraft. Feathering will be simulated by the examiner (zero thrust procedure) on completion of the correct touch drills by the candidate.

(f) Flight with Asymmetric Power

(i) Control of the aeroplane and maintenance of a nominated heading and asymmetric climbing speed following the failure of one engine in the climbing configuration at normal climbing power.

(ii) Identification of the failed engine and the completion of all essential drills and checks.

(iii) Climbing and level turns in asymmetric flight as directed by the examiner.

Tolerances

To pass the test candidates must demonstrate their ability to fly safely at the limits listed below. These limits must not be achieved at the expense of smoothness and proper co-ordination. The following limits relate to calm air; the examiner will make due allowance for turbulent conditions.

	Normal flight	Limited panel flight	Asymmetric flight
Height:			
1. In level flight	+/–100 ft	+/–200 ft	+/–200 ft
2. For initiating a Missed Approach procedure from Decision Height	– 0 ft +50 ft	N/A	N/A
Tracking on Radio Aids:	VOR +/–5° ADF +/–10°	N/A	N/A
Heading:	+/–10°	+/–15°	+/–10°
Speed:	+/–10 kt*	+20 kt –10 kt*	+/–10 kt*
	***Not below threshold speed**		
ILS Approach:	½-scale deflection on localizer and glidepath		

Renewal Flight Test

The IMC Rating *Certificate of Test* is valid for a period of 25 months and it must then be renewed by a flight test with an authorized examiner. The test will comprise items (b), (c), (d) and (e) as outlined for the initial test with the exception that a ground-interpreted aid may be used, provided the previous test included a pilot-interpreted aid. The type of approach aid used during the test must be entered in the log book.

Some Advice on How to Pass the Test

Bearing in mind that it requires of the often inexperienced pilot near-professional levels of skill it would be idle to pretend that the IMC Rating test is undemanding. Having said that there are a number of techniques at the disposal of the candidate which can contribute greatly to passing the test on the first attempt. A good test will be profoundly influenced by:

1. A proper understanding of the examiner's briefing and thorough pre-flight preparation.
2. Good cockpit management, e.g. the orderly arrangement of charts, flight log and such equipment as the watch, protractor, check lists etc.
3. Accurate assessment of the wind, e.g. what may be a correct drift allowance at FL40 will not be the same while flying a hold at 2000 ft.
4. Fluent liaison with ATC. If any instructions are not clear get the position clarified.
5. Being ready for the unexpected. For example, if the departure is not as expected be prepared to select frequencies and navigation aids which will assist compliance and mentally adjust the flight plan.
6. Not being put off if the examiner makes some notes during the test. It may be that you have done something well and he wishes to comment later. Or perhaps he has just remembered to buy the fish for supper!
7. The ability to avoid self-assessment which has ruined many a test. If you do make a mistake, correct it and do not dwell on it; that is time wasting and distracting.
8. Keeping the examiner informed. Never assume that he knows when, for example, you turn on the pitot heat. Tell him why. Likewise, if a navigation aid begins to behave erratically and a

'no signal' flag appears draw this to the examiner's attention, tell him what it means and say what you intend to do.

9. Remembering to carry out regular icing checks. This is particularly important when changing levels. A practical rule would be every 2000 ft when climbing or descending and every four minutes in the cruise. If the examiner were to warn of ice on the leading edges or elsewhere (real or simulated) would you know how to deal with it?

10. The ability to relax. Almost everyone is apprehensive of the test and the examiner knows it. Nevertheless, make a positive effort to relax; your flying will improve.

11. Careful checking of the altimeter. Remember, the safety of the flight depends on correct settings and so will the outcome of the test. There is no latitude for errors in altimeter settings.

Summary of Weaknesses and/or Fail Points

1. Lack of familiarity with the aircraft.
2. Failing to check the instruments, magnetic compass, radios or navigation equipment.
3. Failing to check the ice protection, including ice warning equipment (when fitted).
4. Failing to check before flight the flying controls and trimmers for full and free movement in the correct sense.
5. Poor cockpit management.
6. Liaison or procedural faults with Air Traffic Control clearances/ instructions or failing to obtain or comply with ATC instructions.
7. Failing to identify radio facilities.
8. Altimeter setting errors.
9. Inaccurate flying leading to tolerances being exceeded.
10. Permitting the airspeed to fall below the minimum agreed during the pre-test briefing.
11. Failing to notice and action any navigation communication or other equipment malfunction.
12. Infringing missed approach and/or noise abatement procedures.
13. Inaccurate safety heights, sectors and approach points.
14. Descending below decision height when required to maintain it.

Finally, this section ends with a statement made at the beginning of the book. The foundation of effective and safe radio navigation is basic instrument flying. Pilots who embark on an IMC Rating course in the hope that their indifferent I/F skills will improve while learning about ADF, VOR etc. have little chance of passing the test.

Appendix II
AERAD Charts and Symbols

For the obvious reason that most radio navigation is conducted out of sight of the surface and with reference to ground-based radio facilities it has been necessary to develop a breed of specialist radio charts to replace topographical maps (although these days a limited amount of radio information is included on these).

Several companies publish radio charts in the form of Airways Manuals, large ring binders holding approach and other charts which may easily be up-dated. This book is illustrated with AERAD charts which are produced by a division of British Airways, and used by that airline and many others as well as a considerable number of charter operators and private owners.

Relevant charts are included to illustrate the procedures explained in the previous chapters. This appendix is a summary of the AERAD system and an explanation of the various chart symbols.

AERAD Flight Guide System

Flight guide systems intended for airline use are produced for most parts of the world. These are amended at weekly intervals and they are intended for use by the airlines, air charter/taxy companies and operators of large corporate aircraft with inter-continental capabilities. In addition, there are AERAD Executive Manuals which have been compiled for the needs of corporate aircraft, air-taxy operators and private owners who do not need worldwide coverage. By way of illustration, the following descriptions refer to the *United Kingdom Executive Manuals*. Others are produced for Scandinavia and Central Europe.

AERAD Supplement

This takes the form of a comprehensive directory giving details of all radio facilities within the area covered. They are listed alphabetically and include aerodrome as well as on-and-off airways radio facilities.

239

A separate *Aerodrome Directory* section lists main runway lengths and strengths. A considerable amount of additional information (radio failure procedure, search and rescue arrangements, radar services etc.) is also included. The supplement provided with the *United Kingdom Executive Manual* is entitled *Europe & Middle East Supplement.* It may be regarded as a comprehensive telephone directory of the air in addition to its value as a reference book covering many of the important services and emergency procedures.

AERAD Radio Navigation Charts

The purpose of these charts is to provide a map of the airways system. They take the form of large sheets folded to display a title page showing the areas covered (the sheets are printed on both sides), the main communications frequencies and a directory of airspace restrictions within the area covered. Date of the chart and whether it is 'Low Altitude' or 'High/Low Altitude' is also shown. The charts are known by a system of letters and numbers, e.g. that covering most of the UK is EUR/1. On the reverse side is EUR/2 (northern France).

No towns, roads or railway lines are shown but coastlines are tinted blue, uncontrolled airspace is light grey and controlled airspace is white with airway centrelines indicated by heavy black lines. Headings in both directions are printed at the ends of these lines, the airway designation is shown in a box and the upper/lower limits appear nearby. Distances between sectors/reporting points are printed near the centrelines. The charts also provide the following information:

- **VOR Stations** shown as a compass rose with an extended magnetic north indicator (to allow use of a purpose-designed AERAD protractor). When the station is co-related with DME a three-leg symbol is included in the centre. Adjacent to the VOR symbol is a panel giving the name of the facility, its identification letters (transmitted in morse), frequency and latitude and longitude which may be used for updating Inertial or VLF long-range navigational equipment which is carried by larger aircraft.
- **Non-Directional Beacons (NDBs).** These are depicted as circular areas of dots with a magnetic north indicator. An information panel similar to the one used for VOR stations is also included. When the identification letters are included within quotes transmission includes an audible tone and the beacon's identification signal can therefore be heard through the aircraft

receiver. Without quotes it will be necessary to add an aural tone by switching on the BFO facility provided on the ADF receiver.

- **Major and some Secondary Aerodromes**
- **Danger/Restricted/Prohibited Areas** which are numbered so that they may be referred to the index on the title page of the chart.
- **FIR Boundaries, Control Zones/Areas and MATZ.**
- **Sector Safe Altitudes** printed in heavy blue numbers.
- **Latitude & Longitude, Magnetic Variation** (faint but wide blue lines) and the scale which is repeated at intervals across the top of the chart.

Area Charts

In areas such as the London, Paris and New York TMA the profusion of radio facilities and general complexity of controlled airspace cannot be shown clearly at the scale used for Radio Navigation Charts. For example, those covering UK are drawn to a scale of approximately 17 nm to the inch, parts of Europe are shown 22.857 nm/inch and the more remote parts of Africa, where radio aids and controlled airspace are few and far between, cover 62.5 nm/inch. Scale is selected for maximum convenience.

To cater for the mass of closely packed detail that must be shown in busy terminal areas large-scale (approximately 8 nm/inch) Area Charts are published. In addition to the information provided on the Radio Navigation Charts the ILS localizer is shown for the main airports.

The Executive Manual

These ring binders carry a number of preliminary pages covering: Aerodrome Availability; General Notes (on using the charts); Legend Specifications; information on the various approach slope indicators; Aerodrome telephone numbers; and a section on Aerodrome Operating Minima which explains the basis on which the individual approach chart minima has been compiled. The manual then contains the charts listed below in alphabetical order. The complete range is only provided for the more important airfields.

The AERAD system has been revised on several occasions and although more and more charts are being brought into line with the latest presentation some of the older style remain. The charts are known by letters followed by a number and those quoted in the following text relate to the latest AERAD charts. For example, charts based on ILS are given the letter 'M' and when there are four runways equipped with the aid they will be covered by charts M1, M2, M3 and M4. Some of the charts now listed only apply to relatively few aerodromes. The most common charts are marked with a *.

*AO: Aerodrome Operating Minima. The collection of charts for each airfield starts with a green coloured sheet giving the weather minima for various classes of aircraft related to each runway and the radio aids provided.

A: Airfield Briefing and Advisory Notices.

B: Special Procedures.

*C: Noise Procedures. When the aerodrome is located near noise-sensitive areas there will be a published Noise Abatement Procedure and this is described on 'C' charts.

*D: Aerodrome Chart. This sheet shows the general layout of the aerodrome, its runway(s), taxiway(s), parking apron, buildings and lighting. There is also a panel giving details of the approach/runway lighting. At the top of the page are the airfield elevation, local magnetic variation, latitude and longitude for the ramp area (for setting up Inertial or Omega/VLF area navigation aids) and the radio frequencies for Ground, Tower and ATIS services.

E: Taxi. Important aerodromes have a more detailed runway and taxiway chart marked in sections for easy location of position while complying with taxi instructions. There may also be additional 'E' charts for use in low visibility.

F: Ramp. As the name implies, these charts illustrate the parking areas in detail.

*G: Standard Instrument Departure (SID) Charts. To ensure that aircraft join the airways system at the correct point and at the correct altitude/level, while avoiding inbound traffic and noise-sensitive areas, major aerodromes have Standard Instrument Departure procedures which vary according to the runway in use and the airway to be joined. SID Charts show these procedures in plan form and describe them in a table printed in the lower portion of each chart.

*H: Standard Instrument Arrival (STAR) Charts. The purpose of these charts is to ensure the smooth flow of traffic so that it may be sequenced for landing without risk or delay. They are also designed to avoid noise-sensitive areas whenever possible. Separate charts are produced according to the direction of joining traffic and the charts include one or more holds for use when traffic considerations necessitate a delay before approach.

J: Departure Terrain.

*K: Radar Vectoring Area. This chart illustrates the area covered by airfield radar, sector safe altitudes, missed approach procedures and action to be taken in the event of lost radio communications.

L: Arrival Terrain. Used for intermediate approach.

*M: ILS Approach Charts. These were described in Chapter 7. They also cover localizer-only procedures (LLZ) and in some cases Back Beam (BB) approaches when the installation allows these to be flown.

*N: VOR Approach Charts. These were described in Chapter 5. They also cover VOR/DME, VORTAC (usually military) VOR/NDB and VOR/L (locator beacon) approaches.

*P: NDB Approach Charts. These were described in Chapter 6. They also cover L (locator beacon) approaches.

*Q: VDF Approach Charts. These were described in Chapter 4.

S: Indirect and Go-around.

T: Visual Charts. For VFR flights to and from aerodromes able to accept such traffic routes will be specified and Visual Charts giving related topographical information are provided.

The AERAD Executive Manual is up-dated in step with the internationally agreed AIRAC (Air Information, Regulation and Control) system which operates on a 28-day cycle. New charts and Supplements are provided along with amendment instructions. Brief details of the revisions are shown on the replacement charts.

Handling Airways Manuals in the Air

Airways Manuals are, by nature, bulky volumes and difficult to manage while flying. Therefore all charts relevant to the flight, including approach charts for the alternate(s), should be extracted at the flight-planning stage for convenience.

Many aircraft have a small clip provided on the control wheel so that the approach chart may conveniently be held within the pilot's area of instrument scan. Radio Navigation and Area Charts are handled like topographical maps and should be folded to reveal the area of operation. Some pilots prefer to hold these charts in clear plastic folders so that marks can be made with suitable crayons.

AERAD SYMBOLS

NEW SPECIFICATION
APPROACH CHART LEGEND

02 FEB 87

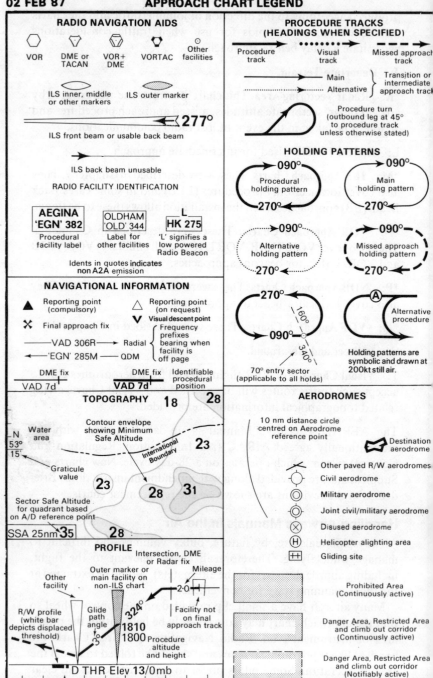

RADIO NAVIGATION AIDS

VOR   DME or TACAN   VOR+DME   VORTAC   Other facilities

ILS inner, middle or other markers   ILS outer marker

◄═ 277°

ILS front beam or usable back beam

ILS back beam unusable

RADIO FACILITY IDENTIFICATION

AEGINA 'EGN' 382
Procedural facility label

OLDHAM 'OLD' 344
Label for other facilities

L HK 275
'L' signifies a low powered Radio Beacon

Idents in quotes indicates non A2A emission

NAVIGATIONAL INFORMATION

▲ Reporting point (compulsory)
△ Reporting point (on request)
✕ Final approach fix
▽ Visual descent point
— VAD 306R → Radial
← 'EGN' 285M — QDM
Frequency prefixes bearing when facility is off page

DME fix VAD 7d
DME fix VAD 7d
Identifiable procedural position

TOPOGRAPHY

18   28

Water area
Contour envelope showing Minimum Safe Altitude
International Boundary
23

N 53° 15'
Graticule value
23

Sector Safe Altitude for quadrant based on A/D reference point
28   31

SSA 25nm 35   28

PROFILE

Other facility
Outer marker or main facility on non-ILS chart
Intersection, DME or Radar fix
Mileage

R/W profile (white bar depicts displaced threshold)
Glide path angle
324°
1810
1800 Procedure altitude and height
2·0
Facility not on final approach track

D THR Elev 13/0mb
2   1   0   1   2   3   4   5

PROCEDURE TRACKS (HEADINGS WHEN SPECIFIED)

Procedure track
Visual track
Missed approach track

— Main
···· Alternative
Transition or intermediate approach track

Procedure turn (outbound leg at 45° to procedure track unless otherwise stated)

HOLDING PATTERNS

090°
Procedural holding pattern
270°

090°
Main holding pattern
270°

090°
Alternative holding pattern
270°

090°
Missed approach holding pattern
270°

270°
090°
70° entry sector (applicable to all holds)
160°
340°

Ⓐ Alternative procedure

Holding patterns are symbolic and drawn at 200kt still air.

AERODROMES

10 nm distance circle centred on Aerodrome reference point

Destination aerodrome
Other paved R/W aerodromes
Civil aerodrome
Military aerodrome
Joint civil/military aerodrome
Disused aerodrome
Ⓗ Helicopter alighting area
Gliding site

Prohibited Area (Continuously active)

Danger Area, Restricted Area and climb out corridor (Continuously active)

Danger Area, Restricted Area and climb out corridor (Notifiably active)

© British Airways AERA

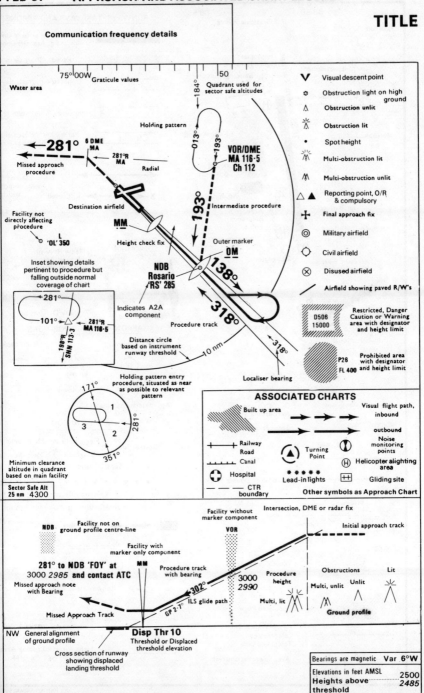

TITLE

Communication frequency details

75° 00W Graticule values   50

Water area

184° Quadrant used for sector safe altitudes

Holding pattern

013°   193°

281° 6 DME MA

281°R MA Radial

Missed approach procedure

VOR/DME MA 116·5 Ch 112

193°   Intermediate procedure

Destination airfield

MM Height check fix

Outer marker
OM

Facility not directly affecting procedure

L 'OL' 350

138°

NDB Rosario 'RS' 285

Inset showing details pertinent to procedure but falling outside normal coverage of chart

281°

101°   281°R MA 116·5

198°R SNN 113·3

318°

Indicates A2A component

318°

Procedure track

Distance circle based on instrument runway threshold

10 nm

Holding pattern entry procedure, situated as near as possible to relevant pattern

171°

1
3   2

281°

351°

Localiser bearing

Visual descent point   V
Obstruction light on high ground
Obstruction unlit
Obstruction lit
Spot height
Multi-obstruction lit
Multi-obstruction unlit
Reporting point, O/R & compulsory
Final approach fix
Military airfield
Civil airfield
Disused airfield
Airfield showing paved R/W's

D506 15000 Restricted, Danger Caution or Warning area with designator and height limit

P26 FL 400 Prohibited area with designator and height limit

ASSOCIATED CHARTS

Built up area

Visual flight path, inbound

outbound

Railway
Road
Canal

Turning Point

Noise monitoring points

Hospital

Helicopter alighting area

CTR boundary

Lead-in lights

Gliding site

Other symbols as Approach Chart

Minimum clearance altitude in quadrant based on main facility

Sector Safe Alt 25 nm 4300

Intersection, DME or radar fix

NDB Facility not on ground profile centre-line

Facility without marker component

VOR Initial approach track

Facility with marker only component

281° to NDB 'FOY' at
3000 *2985* and contact ATC

MM Procedure track with bearing

Obstructions

3000 *2990* Procedure height

Lit

Multi, unlit   Unlit

Missed approach note with Bearing

302° ILS glide path

GP 2·7°

Multi, lit

Ground profile

Missed Approach Track

NW General alignment of ground profile

Disp Thr 10

Threshold or Displaced threshold elevation

Cross section of runway showing displaced landing threshold

Bearings are magnetic Var 6°W

Elevations in feet AMSL 2500
Heights above threshold 2485

Chart Index ➝ **B1**

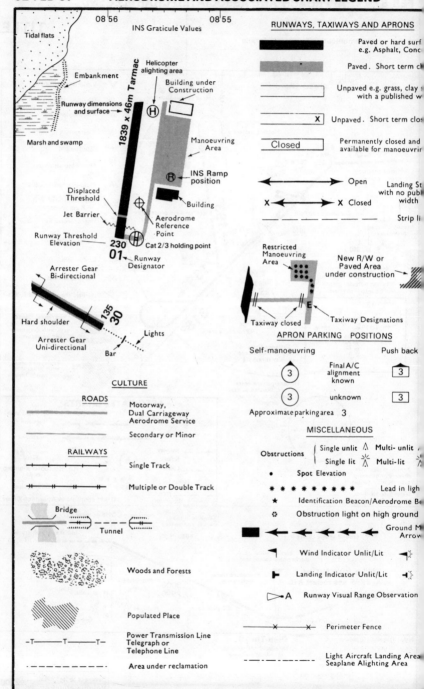

INS Graticule Values · 08 56 · 08 55

Tidal flats

Embankment

Runway dimensions and surface →

1839 × 46m Tarmac

Marsh and swamp

Helicopter alighting area

Building under Construction

Manoeuvring Area

INS Ramp position

Displaced Threshold

Jet Barrier

Runway Threshold Elevation — 230

Building

Aerodrome Reference Point

Cat 2/3 holding point

01 ← Runway Designator

Arrester Gear Bi-directional

Hard shoulder

Arrester Gear Uni-directional

135 / 30

Lights

Bar

RUNWAYS, TAXIWAYS AND APRONS

Paved or hard surf
e.g. Asphalt, Conc

Paved. Short term cl

Unpaved e.g. grass, clay
with a published w

X — Unpaved. Short term clos

Closed — Permanently closed and
available for manoeuvrir

←——————→ Open — Landing St
with no publ
X ←——————→ X Closed — width

———————————— Strip li

Restricted Manoeuvring Area

New R/W or Paved Area under construction

Taxiway closed — E — Taxiway Designations

APRON PARKING POSITIONS

Self-manoeuvring — Push back

(3) Final A/C alignment known — 3

(3) unknown — 3

Approximate parking area 3

CULTURE

ROADS

Motorway, Dual Carriageway Aerodrome Service

Secondary or Minor

RAILWAYS

Single Track

Multiple or Double Track

Bridge

Tunnel

Woods and Forests

Populated Place

-T——T——T- Power Transmission Line Telegraph or Telephone Line

- - - - - - Area under reclamation

MISCELLANEOUS

Obstructions { Single unlit △ Multi- unlit
Single lit ☼ Multi-lit

• Spot Elevation

* * * * * * * * * Lead in ligh

★ Identification Beacon/Aerodrome Be

✿ Obstruction light on high ground

◄ ◄ ◄ ◄ ◄ Ground M
Arrow

◤ Wind Indicator Unlit/Lit ◄

► Landing Indicator Unlit/Lit ◄

▷A Runway Visual Range Observation

——X——X—— Perimeter Fence

— - — - — Light Aircraft Landing Area
Seaplane Alighting Area

© BRITISH AIRWAYS A

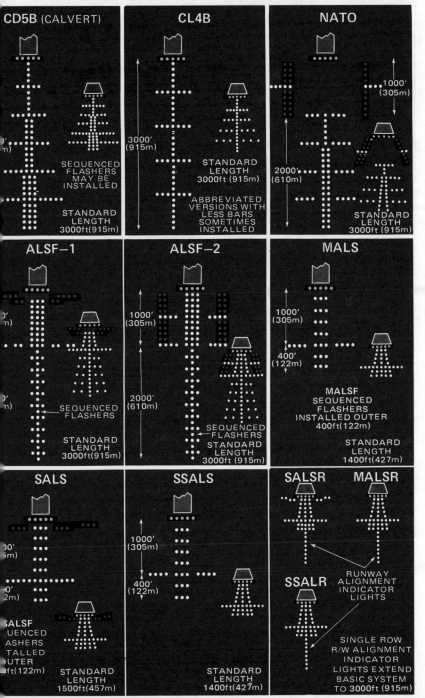

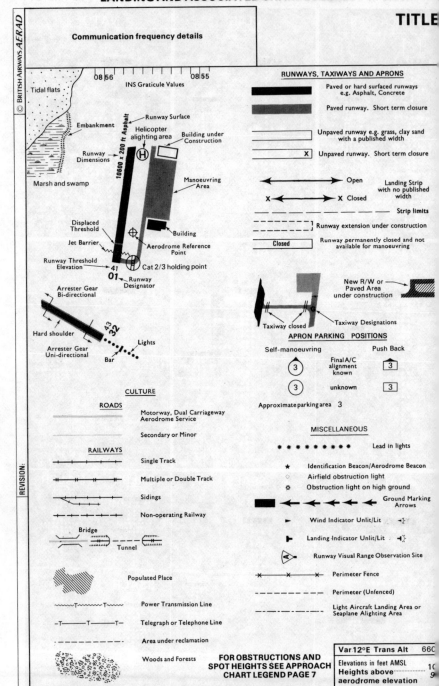

Appendix III
The Phonetic Alphabet

The Phonetic Alphabet

A	Alpha	• —
B	Bravo	— • • •
C	Charlie	— • — •
D	Delta	— • •
E	Echo	•
F	Foxtrot	• • — •
G	Golf	— — •
H	Hotel	• • • •
I	India	• •
J	Juliet	• — — —
K	Kilo	— • —
L	Lima	• — • •
M	Mike	— —

N	November	— •
O	Oscar	— — —
P	Papa	• — — •
Q	Quebec	— — • —
R	Romeo	• — •
S	Sierra	• • •
T	Tango	—
U	Uniform	• • —
V	Victor	• • • —
W	Whisky	• — —
X	X-ray	— • • —
Y	Yankee	— • — —
Z	Zulu	— — • •

Numerals are pronounced

0	Zero		5	Fife
1	Wun		6	Six
2	Too		7	Sev-en
3	Tree		8	Ait
4	Fow-er		9	Nin-er

Tens, hundreds, etc., are spelt out, e.g. 10 is 'wun zero', 650 is 'six fife zero', 25,000 is 'two fife tousand'.

Examples from the 'Q' Code

QDM	Magnetic heading to reach the station with zero wind.
QDR	Reciprocal of QDM.
QFE	Airfield pressure (altimeter reads zero on landing).
QNH	Barometric pressure reduced to mean sea level (altimeter reads airfield altitude a.m.s.l. on landing).
QSY	Change frequency to . . .
QTE	True bearing from station to aircraft.

Index

Index

Index

Index